AN EVALUATION OF CRUDE OIL SUPPLY IN SASKATCHEWAN

James N. Tanner

ii

ISBN-0-920522-44-0

CANADIAN ENERGY RESEARCH INSTITUTE
3512 - 33 STREET N.W.
CALGARY, ALBERTA
T2L 2A6

December 1987

Printed in Canada

Price: $30.00

The Canadian Energy Research Institute is a co-operative research organization sponsored by six parties: Energy, Mines and Resources Canada, the Alberta Department of Energy, the Private Energy Research Association (composed of corporate and individual members from oil, gas, coal, electrical, nuclear energy and pipeline companies), The University of Calgary, the Ontario Ministry of Energy, and the Saskatchewan Department of Energy and Mines. The objectives of the Institute are to develop an economic research capability and to conduct studies that will assist industry and government in dealing with energy problems. The research program of the Institute is developed by a Board of Directors named by the sponsoring organizations. The content of the individual studies is, however, the responsibility of the authors.

CONTENTS

LIST OF FIGURES

LIST OF TABLES

Preface

This study was inspired by the independent research of several different groups. The goal of this study was to integrate the technical expertise of economists, geologists, and engineers to produce a well-rounded work.

Thanks is due to the individuals in the Department of Energy and Mines of the Government of Saskatchewan who contributed in many ways. The contribution of Dr. Ahba Bhargava in the creation of the Disaggregated Drilling Model deserves special mention. Also, we received much input and many useful comments from other economists, engineers, and geologists from that department.

Thanks is also due to the Institute of Sedimentary and Petroleum Geology for the extra work which was done on heavy oil in Saskatchewan and the geological data bases that made our Discovery Model possible. Additional thanks are due to the Federal Department of Energy, Mines and Resources for their interesting suggestions and comments.

The author is particularly grateful to Vance Lickiss who was the model programmer, to Janice Morrison and Michele Irvin who typed the manuscript, and to Lise Henderson and Tony Reinsch for editing and reviewing this study. The author is, however, solely responsible for the conclusions drawn, and for any errors or omissions which are in the study.

EXECUTIVE SUMMARY

The recent volatility of crude oil prices has raised concerns over the volume of oil which can be expected to be discovered in the various supply regions in Canada. This study focuses on the likely implication of crude oil price volatility on future oil supply from the province of Saskatchewan. Currently, Saskatchewan's oil supply is measured by the amount of remaining established reserves in the province. Table I presents these reserves as of December 31, 1985.

TABLE I

REMAINING OIL RESERVES IN SASKATCHEWAN
(million cubic metres)

	1985 Production	Established Reserves (Dec. 31/85)
Area I -- Heavy	3.063	28.074
Area II -- Heavy	0.771	8.180
Area II -- Light	1.218	9.137
Area III -- Medium	1.781	15.205
Area IV -- Medium	2.047	24.186
Area IV -- Light	2.703	27.144
Provincial Total	11.583	111.926

SOURCE: Reserve Annual 1985, Saskatchewan Energy and Mines.

This table presents reserves based upon a specific price assumption. If prices were to change dramatically, the amount of reserves which could actually be recovered may be substantially different.

This study constructed a model to help analyze the effects of price changes on established reserves, and also reserves additions from both new discoveries and extensions of older pools.

The model employs the Saskatchewan Government well data base and research on the royalty rates, taxes, and operation costs in

Saskatchewan to analyze the effects of price changes on established reserves, defined as short-run supply in this study.

The results of this analysis are presented in Table II. The short-run supply of crude oil, which is defined as supply without further exploration or development, does not change dramatically unless prices fall well below the $10 per barrel level.

TABLE II

SHORT-RUN OIL SUPPLY

	Initial Price of Price Forecast ($Cdn.)	Predicted Supply (millions of cubic metres)
Low Case	$10	86
Base Case	$20	104
High Case	$30	106

SOURCE: Canadian Energy Research Institute.

The model was run over a 19-year period to obtain these results. The established reserves for 1985 were 112 million cubic metres. If the base case was run for a longer period, the added production would approximate the established reserves estimate. However, if prices were to fall to the lower price forecast for an indefinite period, Saskatchewan could lose up to 20 million cubic metres of the established reserves.

The long-run analysis includes both current established reserves and reserves which are likely to be discovered in the future. To model future discoveries and additions we made use of the Institute of Sedimentary and Petroleum Geology data on undiscovered pools in Western Canada. These pools were combined with a disaggregated activity model designed by the Saskatchewan Department of Energy and Mines to produce a reserves additions scenario as a function of different oil prices.

In addition to the new pool discoveries, reserves are added through infill and extension drilling on old pools. Analysis of the historical increase of reserves over time was undertaken and estimates were made of the reserves added due to extensions at various prices.

The results of our long-run analysis were divided into two categories, reserves created as a result of new pool discoveries and reserves added due to extensions of previously discovered pools. The results are presented in Table III.

TABLE III

LONG-RUN OIL SUPPLY
(millions of cubic metres)

Initial Price of Price Forecast ($Cdn.)	Short-Run Supply	New Pool Discoveries	Extensions of Old Pools	Total
$10	86	6	23	115
$20	104	10	45	160
$30	106	16	59	181

SOURCE: Canadian Energy Research Institute.

An interesting result of the long-run section of this study is that most future reserves additions are likely to come from extensions of already discovered pools, rather than new discoveries.

Chapter 1

OIL SUPPLY ISSUES

1.1 Introduction

Recent instability in the price of crude oil on international
markets has created considerable uncertainty for the profile of crude
oil supply in Canada. In 1985, Saskatchewan produced over 11 million
cubic metres of oil which represented approximately 16 percent of total
Canadian crude oil production. In the same year, as shown in Table
1.1, Saskatchewan's remaining established reserves were estimated to be
111.926 million cubic metres, yielding a reserves life index of almost
10 years.[1] Given the recent price instability, it is important to
know the likely effects that large changes in crude oil prices would
have on productive capacity and reserve life in Saskatchewan.

TABLE 1.1

REMAINING OIL RESERVES IN SASKATCHEWAN
(million cubic metres)

	1985 Production	Established Reserves (Dec. 31/85)
Area I -- Heavy	3.063	28.074
Area II -- Heavy	0.771	8.180
Area II -- Light	1.218	9.137
Area III -- Medium	1.781	15.205
Area IV -- Medium	2.047	24.186
Area IV -- Light	2.703	27.144
Provincial Total	11.583	111.926

SOURCE: Reservoir Annual, 1985 (Saskatchewan Mineral Resources,
Petroleum and Natural Gas).

This report addresses the question of how Saskatchewan production and reserves would change in response to wide variations in the
price of oil. A major part of this analysis was the creation of an
analytical framework which allows the user to vary prices over time and

observe the estimated effect which such price scenarios will have on the productive capacity and oil reserves of Saskatchewan. This report provides a description of the methodology and results of this modelling exercise and also provides short- and long-run supply curves for conventional oil in Saskatchewan.

1.2 The Model

The focus of this study has been to create and identify short- and long-run supply curves using recently updated data. As these supply curves were being created, an interactive modelling system was developed which accepts non-constant discrete price forecasts. There is an infinite number of possible price forecasts which can be analyzed. The framework developed here allows the user to input a particular price forecast. The model will then respond with the likely short-run supply, productive capacity and long-run supply for the Province of Saskatchewan. This model deals effectively with the various complex intertemporal supply effects of fluctuating oil prices over time.

1.3 Short-Run and Long-Run Supply

Because oil is a non-renewable resource, intertemporal supply is complicated by the division between production from currently discovered reserves and production from reserves which will be discovered in the future.

The short-run analysis estimates the currently established productive capacity and the likely effects of price changes on such capacity. Large increases in price may increase the life of currently producing wells, or allow more expensive well servicing, thus increasing what we define as short-run supply. Large decreases in price may cause wells to be shut-in, or may cause enhanced oil recovery projects to be shut down, resulting in many wells being abandoned and thus decreasing short-run supply. Such an analysis is considered short run only when it does not include changes in capital expenditures.[2]

Long-run supply includes supply from currently discovered resources and supply from new discoveries resulting from future capital expenditures. Each different oil price level implies a level of capital expenditures (exploration and development activity) which in turn generates reserves additions and an increase in productive capacity. These different levels of productive capacity, when totalled over time, generate points on a long-run supply curve.

1.4   Short-Run and Long-Run
Supply Definition

The range of definitions which can be used to estimate short-
and long-run supply of an exhaustible resource leads to misunderstand-
ings. It is important to arrive at a definition which makes sense in
terms of economic theory and practical use. This report proposes such
a definition.

Generally, constraints are imposed in an economic analysis to
allow the observation of variables in isolation and without complex
secondary effects. The major problem is how to apply the economic
definition of short-run, holding one factor of production constant, to
the field of exhaustible resources. To hold capital constant, in a
manufacturing or renewable resource situation, is to assume that a
constant flow of capital is available to the industrial process.[3]
Thus, one can concentrate on the levels of input of other variables.
If, in an exhaustible resource case, we were to assume that a constant
flow of capital were available over time, then a stream of reserves
additions would be generated by that constant capital flow. This
presents a problem. A lower rate of investment would yield a slower
rate of discovery but ultimately the same level of reserves would be
discovered as in a long-run case. It would simply take longer to
discover the same resources.

A further problem when using a definition of short-run supply
with additions and constant capital flow is that of choosing the level
of the flow. If the flow rate is higher (lower) than optimal, the
short-run supply will be higher (lower) than the long-run supply. If
the short-run rate is chosen to be optimal it will be exactly the same
as long-run supply.

To determine the short-run supply of oil in the exhaustible
resource case the definition of constant capital must not allow furthur
capital injections. This will avoid the intertemporal re-allocation of
production capacity which will occur if additions are permitted in a
short-run supply definition. Therefore, the definition of short-run
supply we have used in this study allows no further capital expenditures.

Short-run supply, defined in this way, is equivalent to what
is termed "established" or "proven" reserves. The definition of

established reserves as decided by the Joint Task Force on Uniform Reserves Terminology, November 1978,[4] is as follows:

> Those reserves recoverable under current technology and present and anticipated economic conditions, specifically proved by drilling, testing, or production, plus that judgement portion of contiguous recoverable reserves that are interpreted to exist, from geological, geophysical or similar information, with reasonable certainty.

Estimates of established reserves are undertaken each year by the Province of Saskatchewan. A team of engineers reviews each pool in the province using technical engineering data to estimate the likely continued production and reserves in each pool. These estimates are based on current economic conditions and forecasts of the day. The results of this work are provided each year in the Saskatchewan Reservoir Annual. Estimates and data from the 1985 issue are provided in Table 1.1.

Considerable resources are required to perform this technical analysis on all pools in Saskatchewan for several different economic assumptions. This report provides a less resource-intensive methodology for generating a short-run supply curve by using the Saskatchewan well data base and a computer modelling system as explained in Chapter 2.

Chapters 2 and 3 of this study describe the data, methodology, and results of the short-run analysis of oil supply in Saskatchewan. Chapters 4 and 5 focus on the long-run supply, and Chapters 6, 7, and 8 discuss further results and implications for oil supply in Saskatchewan.

Footnotes

[1]Saskatchewan Energy and Mines, Petroleum and Natural Gas, Reservoir Annual 1985, Miscellaneous Report 86-1 (Regina, Saskatchewan: Saskatchewan Energy and Mines, 1985).

[2]Hal R. Varian, Intermediate Microeconomics, A Modern Approach (New York, N.Y.: W.W. Norton & Company Inc., 1987).

[3]Orris C. Herfindahl and Allen V. Kneese, Economic Theory of Natural Resources (Columbus, Ohio: Charles E. Merrill Publishing Company, 1974).

[4]"Report of the Joint Task Force on Uniform Reserves Terminology," Working paper used internally in the following organizations which were also members of the task force: Government of British Columbia, Government of Alberta, Alberta Energy Resources Conservation Board, Government of Saskatchewan, National Energy Board, Independent Petroleum Association of Canada, Canadian Petroleum Association (November 1978).

Chapter 2

SHORT-RUN ANALYSIS

2.1 Methodology

In order to perform a short-run analysis of oil supply in Saskatchewan, a method of measuring the effects of economic changes on the quantity of oil production must first be developed. A reference point for the supply curve is provided by the Saskatchewan Annual Reserve Report estimate of established reserves for 1985, referred to in Chapter 1. Although this estimate is as accurate as possible, repeating this methodology for each point on a supply curve would be extremely resource intensive, necessitating the development of a less costly methodology.

Two proposals for achieving a less costly method were originally suggested. The first was that the province be analyzed on a pool-by-pool basis in a more concise way than that used by the Province of Saskatchewan's reserve report. A major problem with this suggestion is that, although there are only some 400 pools in the reserves data base, operators are more likely to shut in uneconomic wells rather than entire pools. If our economics were based on pools, the units of production would likely be too large to be accurate.

The second proposal was that Saskatchewan be analyzed on a well-by-well basis. This method would definitely be more accurate. However, this method could prove to be too detailed and the volume of data analysis and processing might prove to be overwhelming. It was therefore decided that the province should be divided into several classes of wells having similar characteristics in order to avoid undertaking an analysis of each individual well.

2.2 Data

The Saskatchewan Government maintains up-to-date records of the oil, natural gas, and water production of each well in Saskatchewan. This data base also classes wells by royalty status, location, region, unit, pool, type of oil, and other factors. Operating costs, taxes, and actual freehold royalty rates are not included in the data base.

However, these factors are very important in the short-run economics of oil production.

Data on operating costs were obtained from estimates developed by independent consultants. These estimates were compared with similar estimates provided by Saskatchewan Energy and Mines. Averages of taxes and freehold royalties were also estimated based on information obtained from independent consultants.[1] This data was then used in the assessment of production economics for producing wells in the province.

2.3 Marginal Production Rates

The key concept in our short-run analysis and a building block in our long-run analysis is the Marginal Production Rate, defined as the production rate at which any given well is likely to be shut in. This rate is defined as the point at which net revenues from operation of the well equal total operating costs.

The production rate multiplied by an oil price generates gross revenue. From this amount, royalties, taxes, and overriding charges must be subtracted. If the net value remaining is not equal to or greater than the cost of operating the well, including periodic maintenance, the well is losing money in the short run and should be shut in. The marginal production rate is calculated as follows:

$$\text{Marginal Production Rate} = \frac{\text{Operating Costs}}{1-(\text{Royalties and Taxes})} \Big/ \text{Price, or;} \tag{1}$$

Rearranging terms yields an expression for operating costs:

$$\text{Operating Costs} = \text{Marginal Production Rate} \times \text{Price} \times 1-(\text{Royalties and Taxes}) \tag{2}$$

Operating costs are defined as a function of the production rates of both oil and water. Therefore, given the necessary data, calculation of the marginal production rate involves solving a simultaneous equation system including equations 2 and 3.

$$\text{Operating Costs} = C + B \left(\begin{array}{c} \text{Production} \\ \text{of Oil} \end{array} \right) + D \left(\begin{array}{c} \text{Production} \\ \text{of Water} \end{array} \right) \tag{3}$$

These equations, in particular equations (1) and (3), were used in calculating marginal production rates in each class in Table 2.1. Further discussion of the process is provided in Chapter 3.

2.4 Designing Well Classifications

In order to reduce the number of calculations required in analyzing over 14,000 wells under several different price assumptions, the wells are divided into homogenous groups. The grouping is done in such a way as to avoid the creation of systematic biases which would create large errors in the results. The royalty classifications are straightforward: there are only two major categories, freehold and Crown. We had to assume an average freehold royalty[2] but the freehold taxes and actual Crown royalties were provided. The royalty/tax status categories were: (1) Exempt from royalties, Crown; (2) Exempt from royalties, freehold; (3) New oil and Crown royalty; (4) Old oil and Crown royalty; (5) New oil and freehold royalty; (6) Old oil and freehold royalty; (7) Crown royalty and Enhanced Oil Recovery (EOR) status; and (8) Freehold royalty and EOR status.

The most complex classifications involved choosing the operating cost categories. Because of the similarity of the geographical conditions, the four areas defined in the Saskatchewan regional well data base were appropriate for use as operating cost classes. Two of the areas were further divided by level of oil quality--heavy and light/medium. This resulted in six basic average operating cost regions. The six regions are: (1) Lloydminster Heavy; (2) Kindersley/Kerrobert Heavy; (3) Swift Current Medium; (4) Weyburn/Estevan Medium; (5) Kindersley/Kerrobert Light; and (6) Weyburn/Estevan Light.

Operating costs vary dramatically across the six regions, depending largely upon the volume of water production experienced by the individual wells. Operating costs are a direct function of water production and there exists a different water production rate for each well. Given the number of wells, the volume of calculations could potentially mushroom again. To avoid this problem, three water production categories were created for each area based upon the average water production in the data base. The resulting 72 final categories are presented in Table 2.1. The assumed water classifications and operating costs for each region are presented in Chapter 3. The description of each royalty classification chosen is also included in Chapter 3.

TABLE 2.1

WELL CLASSIFICATIONS BY AREA

Royalty/ Tax Status	Water Production	Lloydminster Heavy	Kindersley and Kerrobert Heavy	Swift Current Medium	Weyburn Estevan Medium	Kindersley Kerrobert Light	Weyburn Estavan Light
Exempt	Low	*	*	*	*	*	*
	Medium	*	*	*	*	*	*
	High	*	*	*	*	*	*
New Crown	Low	*	*	*	*	*	*
	Medium	*	*	*	*	*	*
	High	*	*	*	*	*	*
Old Crown	Low				*		*
	Medium				*		*
	High				*		*
New Freehold	Low	*	*	*	*	*	*
	Medium	*	*	*	*	*	*
	High	*	*	*	*		*
Old Freehold	Low				*		*
	Medium				*		*
	High						*
Crown EOR	Low	*					
	Medium	*					
	High	*					
Freehold EOR	Low	*					
	Medium	*					
	High	*					

SOURCE: Canadian Energy Research Institute.

2.5 Classification, Decline Rates, Comparison, Summation

2.5.1 Classification

Once the marginal rate categories were established, each well in the data base was classified into a particular group for comparison with marginal rates. In the case of royalty exempt wells, the classification changes when the period of royalty exemption expires. Therefore, each well was classified in each year of the simulation. The royalty exemptions period is assumed to finish at the end of the year in which the exemption expires.

2.5.2 Decline Rates

Within each area defined in the Saskatchewan data base, wells tend to exhibit similar decline characteristics because of the similar oil qualities and similar plays located within each area. Although the decline rates of each well are difficult to predict and current production rates are not uniform across all wells, for simplicity we have assumed that every well within a given area declines at the same constant percentage rate. While this is bound to introduce some errors with individual wells, the aggregate decline is fairly representative of the given area or region.

The decline rates which are used are presented in Table 2.2.

TABLE 2.2

DECLINE RATES FOR OIL WELLS BY AREA
(in percent per year)

Lloydminster Heavy	Kindersley/ Kerrobert Heavy	Swift Current Medium	Weyburn/ Estevan Medium	Kindersley/ Kerrobert Light	Weyburn/ Estevan Light
11.0	8.20	10.0	7.20	9.40	9.0

SOURCE: Canadian Energy Research Institute.

2.5.3 Comparison

In order to decide whether or not a certain well should be shut in, its actual or forecast production rate must be compared with the marginal rate of a particular class. Once the well has been classified and declined, the rate of production is compared with the appropriate marginal rate and either added to the appropriate production category or deemed to be shut in.

2.5.4 Summation

The classification process provides for 72 different classes. This allows considerable flexibility in disaggregating the effects of any particular price assumption. In the output presented in Appendix C, totals are presented in the following subcategories:

- by region or area, and
- by royalty category.

More detailed output can be obtained by dividing the wells by water cateogory. To display these results using the current system would require additional programming.

2.5.5 Flowchart

A flowchart showing the short-run supply process is presented in Figure 2.1.

The two major inputs to the short-run system are the Saskatchewan well data base file and the economic inputs section. The Saskatchewan well data base may be updated as new production months are added by the Government of Saskatchewan. The economic inputs may be changed each time the model is run. The prices of oil and gas, regional operating costs and inflation rates are required by the Resource Analysis Model to calculate the marginal production rates.

The Resource Analysis Model calculates marginal production rates for each category, shown in Table 2.1. These rates are then used in the "Compare" process in CLASS.PRG, represented in the centre of the flowchart in Figure 2.1. CLASS.PRG contains "Classify," "Decline," "Compare," and "Sum" as described in previous paragraphs. These operations are performed on the wells in the Saskatchewan well data base. Some wells are eliminated by the process each year. The remainder are totalled and presented in yearly totals in the results section. Three separate runs, each using different oil price assumptions, are presented at the end of this chapter in section 2.6.

13

FIGURE 2.1   SASKATCHEWAN CONVENTIONAL OIL SUPPLY
SHORT RUN SUPPLY FLOW CHART

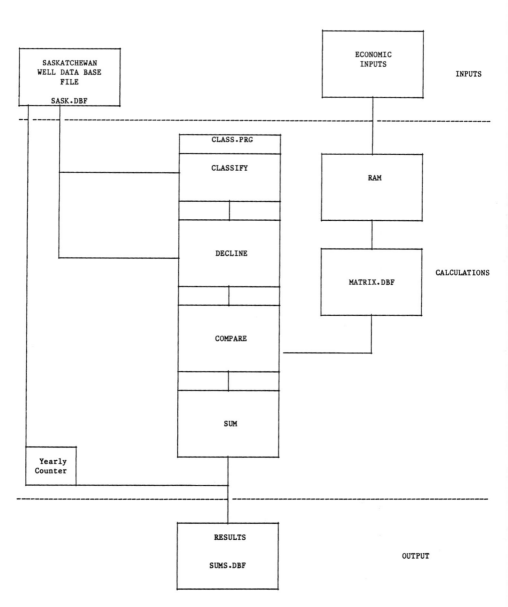

SOURCE: Canadian Energy Research Institute.

TABLE 2.3

SHORT-RUN SUPPLY
LOW CASE
(cubic metres)

Year	Area 1 Totals	Area 2 Totals	Area 3 Totals	Area 4 Totals	Area 5 Totals	Area 6 Totals	Total of Totals
1986	2 974 555.20	804 318.00	1 866 295.20	2 241 174.00	1 219 914.00	2 902 586.40	12 008 842.80
1987	2 378 391.14	704 608.70	1 657 296.72	2 010 794.12	1 074 027.48	2 538 805.00	10 363 923.17
1988	1 526 077.92	574 312.70	1 415 247.55	1 556 842.22	918 781.43	1 958 811.94	7 950 073.76
1989	1 252 188.23	510 441.08	1 256 583.71	1 409 605.54	818 174.86	1 727 049.08	6 974 042.50
1990	1 051 630.98	478 098.25	1 114 326.27	1 307 592.43	744 583.00	1 563 961.72	6 260 192.65
1991	967 587.06	441 762.25	985 846.44	1 228 958.42	675 491.74	1 437 984.24	5 636 630.15
1992	851 544.83	392 542.87	872 958.80	1 108 378.64	599 294.23	1 270 194.96	5 094 914.34
1993	697 249.14	367 834.72	770 172.42	1 010 995.62	529 587.46	1 121 763.73	4 497 603.08
1994	574 102.50	323 192.08	672 760.33	920 849.72	467 067.52	991 584.25	3 949 556.40
1995	468 365.69	297 610.40	594 494.41	876 329.39	409 484.32	888 147.60	3 534 431.81
1996	373 208.90	269 685.01	521 638.14	799 266.72	356 977.44	818 278.99	3 139 055.21
1997	309 757.61	236 902.42	506 343.82	741 573.95	309 770.40	726 987.61	2 831 335.80
1998	249 585.19	210 095.87	445 100.71	672 779.33	265 805.36	644 407.41	2 487 773.88
1999	199 755.46	184 992.56	392 291.84	624 252.90	226 667.96	587 490.42	2 215 451.15
2000	235 154.81	162 640.97	344 202.48	566 640.28	190 237.93	510 534.43	2 009 410.90
2001	193 198.42	142 541.22	316 488.94	523 450.37	161 334.40	448 923.08	1 785 936.42
2002	156 405.10	125 786.82	277 430.26	474 430.51	133 749.82	405 934.30	1 573 736.80
2003	123 989.96	109 727.12	242 435.46	440 849.30	110 386.03	361 662.63	1 389 050.52
2004	117 336.89	95 478.85	211 542,84	398 923.90	90 519.04	311 403.24	1 225 204.75
2005	91 946.29	80 796.20	104 162.12	369 898.76	69 818.16	286 938.43	1 093 559.98
Totals	14 792 031.31	6 513 368.11	14 657 618.47	19 283 586.13	9 371 672.56	21 503 449.48	86 121 726.06

SOURCE: Canadian Energy Research Institute.

TABLE 2.4

SHORT-RUN SUPPLY
BASE CASE
(cubic metres)

Year	Area 1 Totals	Area 2 Totals	Area 3 Totals	Area 4 Totals	Area 5 Totals	Area 6 Totals	Total of Totals
1986	2 974 555.20	804 318.00	1 866 295.20	2 241 174.00	1 219 914.00	2 902 586.40	12 008 842.80
1987	2 277 712.96	701 507.69	1 654 310.52	2 000 765.03	1 083 998.20	2 514 061.37	10 332 355.76
1988	2 098 994.34	642 442.90	1 486 371.71	1 851 758.83	978 949.38	2 269 006.57	9 327 523.73
1989	1 827 841.24	583 241.88	1 332 877.66	1 715 629.94	881 746.79	2 040 681.42	8 372 018.93
1990	1 616 619.08	538 213.88	1 195 781.62	1 592 159.77	801 134.75	1 863 248.63	7 607 177.74
1991	1 388 789.09	495 803.83	1 078 304.41	1 478 151.12	726 194.89	1 692 251.67	6 859 494.96
1992	1 259 479.61	454 108.72	968 720.86	1 372 245.41	653 769.38	1 537 272.28	6 245 596.45
1993	1 088 944.85	416 946.95	871 164.04	1 273 063.94	590 320.01	1 391 748.01	5 632 187.79
1994	970 872.38	381 915.42	783 285.20	1 181 019.85	350 058.35	1 265 047.78	5 112 198.98
1995	852 948.13	350 451.68	700 806.00	1 096 669.37	480 459.41	1 147 772.94	4 629 197.53
1996	727 370.14	319 441.38	631 557.64	1 011 699.95	430 708.80	1 031 952.10	4 152 729.97
1997	643 288.55	293 781.89	565 795.61	942 692.37	385 444.92	941 348.04	3 772 351.38
1998	559 086.20	268 414.33	509 577.66	869 934.24	343 291.92	846 173.87	3 396 478.22
1999	483 267.36	246 869.96	456 366.38	809 290.45	319 610.40	767 290.17	3 082 694.74
2000	410 298.35	226 502.38	407 722.92	747 277.72	286 041.10	692 423.00	2 770 265.46
2001	369 068.62	205 660.04	368 635.63	696 994.80	255 694.52	623 103.97	2 518 178.59
2002	310 953.38	186 632.29	329 200.22	641 182.80	227 229.02	561 707.22	2 256 904.92
2003	276 726.34	173 106.46	293 499.66	592 890.47	210 730.44	514 693.45	2 061 646.81
2004	227 662.92	156 867.90	266 093.11	551 545.78	187 586.14	459 671.41	1 849 427.26
2005	203 562.84	144 487.19	237 366.74	510 538.76	166 722.57	418 046.45	1 680 724.55
Totals	20 658 041.58	7 590 714.74	16 003 732.79	23 175 694.61	10 759 624.98	25 480 086.70	103 667 895.40

SOURCE: Canadian Energy Research Institute.

TABLE 2.5

SHORT-RUN SUPPLY
HIGH CASE
(cubic metres)

Year	Area 1 Totals	Area 2 Totals	Area 3 Totals	Area 4 Totals	Area 5 Totals	Area 6 Totals	Total of Totals
1986	2 974 555.20	804 318.00	1 866 295.20	2 241 174.00	1 219 914.00	2 902 586.40	12 008 842.80
1987	2 377 712.96	701 507.69	1 654 310.52	2 000 765.03	1 083 998.20	2 514 061.37	10 332 355.76
1988	2 210 470.38	657 163.94	1 500 064.27	1 892 163.50	989 453.45	2 339 989.99	9 589 305.54
1989	1 933 729.68	599 841.61	1 347 716.00	1 755 927.74	893 506.10	2 125 557.62	8 656 278.77
1990	1 719 759.80	552 062.46	1 213 162.49	1 628 351.10	808 747.62	1 930 689.35	7 852 772.82
1991	1 503 145.49	506 793.35	1 089 653.87	1 511 311.34	733 287.92	1 753 185.37	7 097 377.34
1992	1 340 127.14	463 400.60	978 031.06	1 399 518.69	662 492.63	1 584 022.00	6 427 592.03
1993	1 178 066.92	425 715.59	877 057.42	1 296 064.07	598 067.54	1 443 456.77	5 818 428.30
1994	1 041 957.73	388 741.85	792 087.90	1 204 885.96	539 045.84	1 303 879.15	5 270 598.43
1995	919 699.86	358 044.00	710 143.62	1 117 312.18	491 838.31	1 186 852.91	4 783 889.98
1996	798 367.16	326 769.68	637 885.73	1 036 175.65	443 367.02	1 074 122.59	4 316 687.84
1997	703 841.72	299 960.53	572 019.98	959 099.22	399 261.38	973 298.62	3 907 481.47
1998	612 991.56	274 949.41	512 942.08	891 913.02	357 473.39	879 404.20	3 529 842.66
1999	537 316.52	250 701.35	458 700.73	824 819.81	325 366.30	798 536.20	3 195 340.91
2000	467 122.85	231 396.77	411 391.62	763 301.39	291 696.50	722 124.90	2 887 034.03
2001	410 291.95	210 735.01	367 250.77	710 808.66	266 379.95	656 722.79	2 622 188.44
2002	347 863.81	194 256.65	327 070.56	657 281.96	238 312.97	592 639.49	2 358 325.44
2003	308 566.70	176 155.57	292 400.95	610 370.70	213 830.50	539 511.55	2 140 835.98
2004	266 858.45	162 427.25	260 062.01	564 745.14	190 697.26	585 308.63	1 930 098.73
2005	234 062.21	148 255.00	230 524.57	521 830.92	171 768.64	439 155.41	1 745 596.74
Totals	21 886 508.11	7 733 196.31	16 099 670.65	23 587 819.00	10 918 575.53	26 245 104.90	106 470 873.40

SOURCE: Canadian Energy Research Institute.

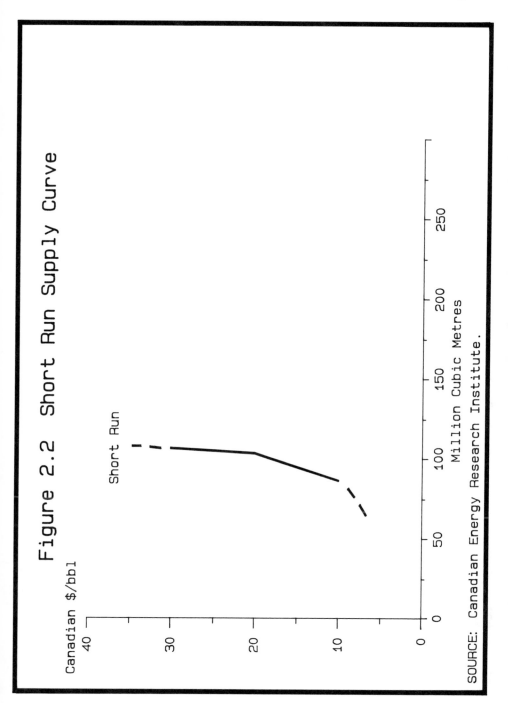

Figure 2.2 Short Run Supply Curve

Canadian $/bbl

Short Run

Million Cubic Metres

SOURCE: Canadian Energy Research Institute.

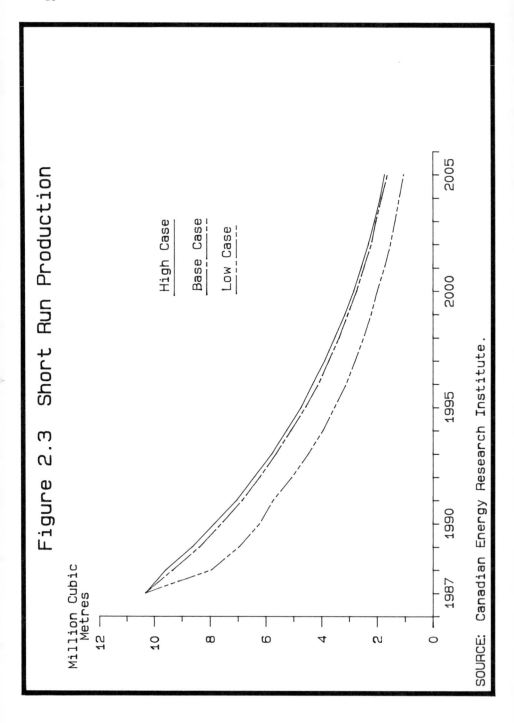

Figure 2.3 Short Run Production

Million Cubic Metres

High Case

Base Case

Low Case

SOURCE: Canadian Energy Research Institute.

2.6 Choice of Price Assumptions

Since this computer-based supply system can run over a 50-year time period, it is important to choose both a current range of prices and an escalation rate for alternative scenarios. The initial choices we made were average wellhead prices for Saskatchewan of $10, $20, and $30 ($Cdn./bbl) for 1987. This range of prices is currently of interest to policy makers and tends to give a broad enough range to test some limits of the model. These initial prices were then inflated and in some cases escalated in future years. The escalations used were 4 percent inflation plus up to 2 percent real growth in prices for the high and medium cases and no real growth for the low case. The case prices used are presented in Appendix A. The reader should note that references in this text to prices of $10, $20, and $30 per barrel are references to only the initial prices of the forecast described above.

2.7 Short-Run Supply Results

The time frame assumed for these first runs was 19 years. The totals are, therefore, for 19 years of production. These estimates do not represent total established reserves estimates, since some wells would be expected to continue producing for up to 30 years. An estimate of total established reserves is provided in Chapter 1, Table 1.1, for comparison. The results of the runs are provided below in Tables 2.3 (Low case), 2.4 (Base case), and 2.5 (High case).

2.8 Analysis

Figure 2.2 shows the short-run supply curve which is generated by these results and Figure 2.3 shows production over time given the three price scenarios. The low case represents the price of oil in a competitive environment where OPEC has been unable to restrain production. The base case represents the continuance of the status quo with expected inflationary pressures. The short-run elasticity between the low case ($10) and the base case ($20) is .379. This represents a 38 percent change in Saskatchewan's capacity to produce its existing discoveries if the world price falls to a competitive floor. The difference in the high price and base case gives an elasticity of .076. This represents marginal production which may be activated if prices were to rise substantially. It should be noted that these estimates do not include any additional capital investment. The short-run analysis refers only to discovered resources.

20

Footnotes

[1]Brian Van Marion, an independent consultant, conducted a study of various operating costs in the province. Using this data he constructed estimates of average costs in each region which were taken into consideration when the model coefficients were set.

[2]The Saskatchewan data base contains a code which identifies wells as being located in one of four regions and producing either light/medium or heavy oil, and designates wells as either freehold or Crown. Freehold royalties may vary according to private arrangements. The actual assumptions are outlined in section 3.1.3.

Chapter 3

ROYALTY AND COST CATEGORIES*

3.1 Royalty and Mineral Tax Classifications

For the purposes of calculating the marginal production rates, certain royalty and tax assumptions were made. These assumptions were designed to be as consistent with current government policy as possible.

In the analysis framework, Saskatchewan royalties and production taxes are applied to oil production and are treated as costs in the calculation of the minimum economic oil production volume or marginal production rate.

The general equations for this calculation are presented in section 2.3 of this study. A different royalty rate has been used for each different classification presented below. For this exercise, wells in the database are classified into 1 of 8 royalty tax categories. The eight categories used are:

(1) Crown Exempt
(2) Freehold Exempt
(3) New Crown
(4) Old Crown
(5) New Freehold
(6) Old Freehold
(7) Crown EOR
(8) Freehold EOR

These categories are used to represent all existing classifications as per current (January 1, 1987) Saskatchewan Petroleum and Natural Gas Regulations and Freehold Oil and Gas Production Tax Regulations. The categories were established in such a way that the economic impact of the various existing classifications could be distinguished and assessed independently while minimizing the number of categories required.

---

*Mike Kirkegaard, of CERI Energy Research Ltd., contributed considerably to this chapter.

In addition to the grouping of different royalty types within certain categories, several assumptions were made with respect to the rate of royalty or tax for certain categories. Well groupings and assumptions made are discussed in the following paragraphs.

3.1.1 Exempt Categories

The Crown exempt category includes all working interest owner exempt, federal lands exempt, and those Crown wells which qualify for royalty holidays (wells in the Crown exempt category are not subject to any form of production burden).

The freehold exempt category includes all freehold wells exempt from the freehold production tax. These wells do not pay the freehold production tax but are burdened with a 15 percent gross royalty which represents the assumed average rate payable to freehold land owners in the province.

3.1.2 Crown and Crown-Acquired Categories

The New Crown category includes Crown and Crown-acquired wells with new oil status. Crown and Crown-acquired wells are grouped together because they result in approximately equal Crown charges payable despite having separate treatment according to existing regulations. The Crown-acquired royalty is equal to the Crown-acquired lease rate plus the calculated Crown royalty rate and minus a production tax factor, where the production tax factor is equal to the Crown-acquired lease rate. Therefore, the net result is the Crown royalty rate, and Crown royalties are equivalent to the Crown-acquired royalties. The old Crown category was established to recognize the substantially higher rates of royalty levied on old wells than those for new wells.

3.1.3 Freehold Categories

The new and old freehold categories are subject to freehold production taxes and to a 15 percent gross royalty payable to the freehold landowner. The calculation of the freehold production tax for freehold wells is very similar to that for Crown-acquired wells except that the net burden for freehold wells is, on average, significantly higher. As is the case for Crown-acquired wells, freehold wells are allowed to subtract a production tax factor (PTF) from the calculated

Crown royalty in lieu of the lease burden payable to the landowner. However, for freehold royalties the production tax factors for old and new wells are set values of 6.9 and 10.0 percent, respectively, and not the freehold landowner lease rate which is typically 15 percent. Therefore, the net result is that an average freehold well will pay a higher rate of royalty than a Crown or Crown-acquired well at the margin when production is shut in.

3.1.4 Enhanced Oil Recovery

EOR wells are subject to a substantially different royalty regime than are conventional wells. EOR royalties/taxes are profit sensitive with variable rates depending on the payout status of the well and on lease ownership category. All EOR wells are assumed to have pre-payout status. We have assumed that the pre-payout royalty rate for Crown and Crown-acquired wells is 5 percent and for freehold wells is zero. However, freehold EOR wells have been assessed the average gross overriding royalty payable to the freehold land owner of 15 percent.

These royalty and tax categories were calculated for each of the 6 regions in Saskatchewan, where applicable. The following sections outline the other costs used in the calculation of marginal production rates in these regions.

3.2 Operating Costs

The second cost category mentioned in the equations in section 2.3 is operating costs. A description of the various operating costs used to calculate marginal production rates is presented below.

All wells are subject to three operating cost components: a fixed cost expressed as $/well/month, an oil processing cost, and a water processing cost, both expressed in terms of dollars per cubic metre of oil or water produced. Although the costs can vary as a function of the fluid volume processed and the water disposal costs, the nature of the analysis has led us to approximate costs as a direct function of water and oil volumes separately, for reasons which will become apparent. The operating costs for each area are presented in Table 3.1.

TABLE 3.1

OPERATING COSTS
(1987 $Cdn.)

Physical Area/ Crude Type Class	Fixed Cost ($/well/month)	Oil Processing Cost ($/m³ of oil)	Water Processing and Handling ($/m³ of water)
1	2500	9.45	3.15
2	2500	9.45	3.15
3	1500	14.24	3.15
4	2190	7.81	3.15
5	940	2.02	3.15
6	2190	7.81	3.15

SOURCE: Canadian Energy Research Institute.

These classes are based upon the Saskatchewan data base area and crude type classes which are:

(1) Lloydminster, heavy
(2) Kindersley/Kerrobert, heavy
(3) Swift Current, medium
(4) Weyburn/Estavan, medium
(5) Kindersley/Kerrobert, light
(6) Weyburn/Estavan, light

The costs are based on the quality of oil produced, the region in which the oil is produced, and the nature of water disposal.

In order to avoid having to analyze each well based on two variables—oil and water production—assumptions were required for water production levels. Each area produces a characteristic amount of water and the assumptions made took into consideration the average levels of water production and the current distribution of water production in each area.

In Table 3.2 we present the ranges of water production in cubic metres per well per month in each area. The areas have been divided into three groups in an attempt to have an equal number of existing wells in each water production group. Besides the range, a mean value of water production for the group is provided. For example, in Area 6 the water production range in the low category is from 0 to 138 and the mean value is almost half or 48.3, whereas in Area 5 the range is from 0 to 21 and the mean value is only 0.15. This shows the lack of water production in Area 5 and the fairly frequent level of water production in Area 6.

TABLE 3.2

WATER PRODUCTION BY WATER CLASS
(m^3/well/month)

Physical Area/ Crude Type Class	Low		Medium		High	
	Range	Mean	Range	Mean	Range	Mean
1	0-57	4.50	58-162	82	163+	215
2	0-96	23.50	97-291	169	292+	387
3	0-267	61.30	268-798	506	799+	1063
4	0-105	39.90	106-318	179	319+	423
5	0-21	0.25	22-60	23	61+	80
6	0-138	48.30	139-414	241	415+	551

SOURCE: Canadian Energy Research Institute.

In order to assign costs to these classes of water production the actual water processing costs per well per month had to be calculated. They are presented in Table 3.3.

TABLE 3.3

ESTIMATED WATER PROCESSING
COSTS BY CLASS
(1987 $/well/month)

Physical Area/ Crude Type Class	Low	Medium	High
1	14	258	677
2	74	532	1219
3	193	1594	3348
4	126	564	1332
5	1	72	252
6	152	759	1736

SOURCE: Canadian Energy Research Institute.

An additional cost of $500/well/month is added for EOR wells in the analysis. This is only applied to those wells identified as EOR by the sorting system.

By classifying wells with an actual water production into either a low, medium or high category and then assigning constant water processing costs for each category we are not making complete use of the wealth of data. However, this approximation attempts to measure average water processing costs and in total is unlikely to be greatly biased. Wells with actual water production substantially lower or higher than the average values in each area/class will be shut in sooner or later than the optimal point, but on average the totals should be fairly accurate.

Since operating costs are such an important part of this analysis, it is important to obtain accurate estimates. The water production analysis could be made more accurate by assessing each well on the basis of both water and oil production. However, this process was determined to be too calculation-intensive for the size of this study.

Chapter 4

LONG-RUN ANALYSIS

4.1 Long-Run Supply

In order to estimate long-run supply of oil in Saskatchewan one must be able to forecast the optimal levels of capital stock under several different assumptions concerning price and economic conditions. This optimal capital stock, which implies an optimal rate of investment, will produce a reserves additions scenario which in turn will allow an estimate of productive capacity over time.

It is important to note that these two major relationships are difficult to measure empirically. The first relationship, between economic conditions and an optimal rate of investment, has received a considerable amount of attention recently. Some of the work done in this area is reviewed below and the estimation methods which were used in this model are described in that context.

The second relationship, between quantity of investment and reserves additions or productive capacity, is modelled using a methodology which has a great deal of potential. Earlier methodologies will be reviewed and a complete description of the methodology used in this paper will follow.

Finally, a description of some of the practical estimation problems involved in creating the system will be discussed and the results of the long-run supply estimates will be presented.

4.2 Optimal Capital Stock and Investment

4.2.1 Theory

An exhaustible resource such as oil requires investment or a stock of capital before it can be produced. Oil is not simply an inventory commodity which can be obtained by turning on the tap of some large storage tank, despite the fact that the world is currently able to produce more crude oil than is immediately demanded at current world prices. Maintenance of the production of oil generally requires a certain level of exploration and development expenditures. According to theoretical models, these capital expenditures should be made only if the risk-adjusted returns of making such expenditures are greater than the cost of the required capital. This principle depends upon two major assumptions: perfect capital markets and quantifiable risk.

If the capital markets are not perfect, the theoretical model (which states that investment is a function of the rate of return and an inverse function of the cost of capital) is restricted by the industry's cash flow. Alternatively, if the risk is not quantifiable then the capital markets will be subject to periods of optimism and pessimism, failing to accurately estimate the expected returns which may result from such capital investments. Both of these problems complicate the task of estimating future investment in the oil and gas industry.

The problem of cash flow constraints will cause estimation methods which use only profitability to occasionally over-estimate the likely investment. Alternatively, the inability to forecast market optimism, pessimism, or play cycles experienced in oil exploration will result in estimates which under-estimate the variability experienced in the real world.

4.2.2 Studies of Investment Response

The results of studies which have attempted to deal with these problems have been encouraging. There exists a general consensus that the use of expected profit will tend to produce acceptable results. However, the problems of cash flow constraints still loom in the background.

The problem of estimating exploration activity involves developing a theory of expectations in order to deal with market pessimism or optimism. A straightforward approach was outlined in Scarfe and Rilkof (1984),[1] where a partial adjustment model was specified. While this proved to be an interesting solution, the use of lagged dependent variables as independent variables could result in inconsistent estimates. However, since it is important to retain some partial adjustment or expectations element in the model, a system which replaces the lagged dependent variable with statistical instruments such as geophysical activity or land purchases should avoid this problem.[2] The use of land expenditures as an instrument for exploration drilling is demonstrated in Bing and Gillies (1987).[3]

In order to deal with the imperfect capital markets hypothesis, Scarfe and Rilkof tested cash flow variables against profit variables and concluded that both are significant. Madduri and Tanner (1983)[4] used a hybrid cash flow and profit variable. Bing and Gillies use profitability which can be regulated by a cash flow constraint. The difficulty here is that capital markets seem to be imperfect in the short term but able to adjust in the longer term. This may suggest the use of a distributed lag profit variable, which has been tested by most of these studies.

4.2.3 Saskatchewan Estimates

In order to estimate the likely future investment or number of wells drilled in Saskatchewan, we used a model, designed by the Government of Saskatchewan, which conformed to the expected profit methodology. The Saskatchewan methodology was developed by Dr. Abha Bhargava in a study of Alberta.[5] A disaggregated model was developed for the Province of Saskatchewan by Dr. Bhargava and is described in Chapter 5 of this study.[6] The estimates in this model were made using data which were divided into four areas in order to emphasize the specific regional differences within Saskatchewan. One division which was forfeited by this regional disaggregation was the division between exploration and development drilling. This was estimated, within our system, by using historical averages in each region.

Two problems arising from the methodology which we have used are worthy of note. First, the estimates of expected profit in this model may not adequately account for basin depletion. As a result, the forecasts for later years are likely to be over-estimates. This problem is not easily solved given the difficulty in obtaining econometric results using small samples. The historical data in Saskatchewan have enough variance to provide some confidence in the results of the Saskatchewan Disaggregated Activity Model.

The second problem is that the proportion of exploration and development wells tends to vary considerably from cycle to cycle. Using a constant proportion of exploration and development wells is likely to introduce poor timing effects into the estimates, but should give consistent long-run results. Constant success ratios were assumed for this study. This assumption is not unreasonable given the recent work by John Lohrenz (1987) showing fairly constant success ratios in most basins in the United States.[7]

4.3 Estimate of Reserves Additions:
New Discoveries

4.3.1 Trend Analysis

Long-run supply must include the effects of additional capital injections. Therefore, the exhaustible resource long-run supply curve will be the total of existing discoveries produced over time plus production from future discoveries. The most difficult part of estimating long-run supply becomes estimating future discoveries.

Estimating reserves additions and added production involves some complex problems. Methodologies which have been used in the past involve econometric or trend analysis where prices or profits are regressed against activity and/or added reserves.[8] Simple trend analysis could be appropriate for the short term. However, the nature of an exhaustible resource demands that some measure of a long-term resource limit be included.

4.3.2 Ultimate Potential

An advanced methodology which combines this historical trend analysis with geological information involves the use of estimates of ultimate potential in the regression equation.[9] Ultimate potential is a geological-based estimate of the likely reserves to be ultimately recoverable from a particular area. A simple example of this methodology is shown below:

$$Y = U (1-e^{BX})$$

Y = cumulative reserves
U = ultimate potential
X = cumulative drilling effort

Using this methodology a coefficient B can be estimated and fitted to a curve using ultimate potential (U). The change in cumulative reserves from period to period is the forecast of added reserves over time.

Including geological inputs in our analysis greatly enhances the reasonability of the results. However, such equations tend to produce smooth curves. History shows that additions and new discoveries tend to come in uneven accumulations which may or may not show a noticeable decline over time. The nature of additions seems to indicate that they depend on both the size and frequency of new discoveries.

4.3.3 Geological Methods and Pool Size Distributions

Recently, the Geological Survey of Canada (GSC) has designed a methodology for estimating ultimate potential which may provide solutions to some of these problems. They have devised a system which forecasts the likely pool sizes remaining to be discovered in each play in Western Canada. This methodology was used to generate an estimate of the future discoveries of crude oil in Saskatchewan.

The GSC modelling system classifies existing pools into play definitions. Each play definition is then analysed using the assumption that the pool sizes within that play fit a log normal distribution. The log normal curve is then estimated using the existing pool data and other geological inputs. The results of such an estimate provide likely pool sizes for undiscovered pools within each play. An example of such a log normal distribution is presented in Figure 4.1.

Given the likely spectrum of pool sizes within each play, the discovery of these pools can be predicted. The expected production which will be forthcoming from these pools is also more predictable given the additional knowledge of pool parameters such as size and average play characteristics. Reserves additions and supply from exploration activity can therefore be estimated more easily and more accurately.

In order to accomplish this, a forecast of the number of successful exploration wells is required. This forecast comes from the Saskatchewan Energy Model (SEM) described in the previous section. New pools are likely to be discovered in proportion to their relative sizes. The hypothesis is that the larger pools tend to be discovered first, because the larger areal extent provides a larger target and because the explorationists have added incentive to find larger pools. Using historical data, tests can be made to determine to what extent larger pools are discovered early in any particular play history.

32

FIGURE 4.1

CARDIUM - MARINE SCOUR - FILL PLAY,
UPPER CRETACEOUS WESTERN CANADA

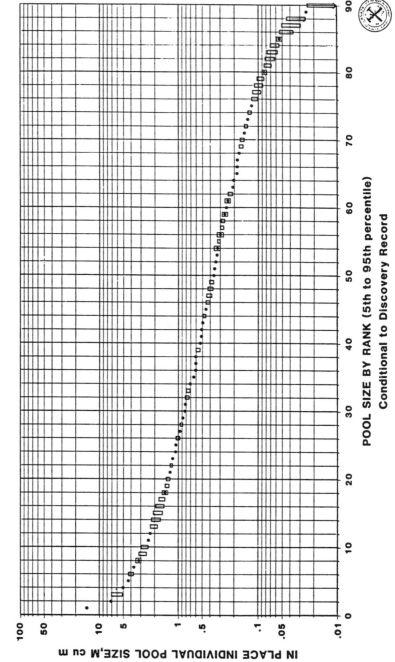

POOL SIZE BY RANK (5th to 95th percentile)
Conditional to Discovery Record

SOURCE: Internal Graph from Institute of Sedimentary and Petroleum
Geology.

4.3.4 Sampling Without Replacement

The Discovery Model, which is known as the sampling without replacement methodology, first suggested for these purposes by Gordon Kaufman et al (1975),[10] was used by P. J. Lee et al[11] of the GSC in its generalized form. Dr. Lee hypothesized that the probability of discovering one particular pool was proportionate to the relative pool sizes, scaled by an exponent B.

Kaufman's original model:

$$P_i \; \alpha \; \frac{\text{Pool Size}_i}{\sum \text{Pool Size}_i}$$

Generalized form:

$$P_i \; \alpha \; \frac{(\text{Pool Size}_i)^B}{\sum (\text{Pool Size}_i)^B}$$

The exponent, B (Beta) represents the degree to which larger pools are discovered first. If B = 1, the probability of discovery is exactly proportionate to the pool sizes (equivalent to Kaufman's original model). If B = 0, the process is completely random. The larger B becomes, the greater is the likelihood that larger pools will be discovered early in the life of the basin. This process was used to determine the order in which existing undiscovered pools are discovered in this modeling system.

4.3.5 The Institute of Sedimentary and
       Petroleum Geology (ISPG) Pool Size
       Distributions for Saskatchewan

In order to allow us to complete an analysis of future discoveries in Saskatchewan, the ISPG provided estimates of remaining undiscovered pools in Saskatchewan for both light/medium and heavy oil plays. This required additional work developing distributions of heavy oil pools. This was done through cooperation with Malcolm Wilson of Saskatchewan Energy and Mines.[12] CERI was provided with ten different play classifications of light/medium oils and four play classifications of heavy oil. These undiscovered pools numbered in the hundreds and were located across the 6 regions in Saskatchewan. A description of each play used in the ISPG data base is included in Appendix D.

4.4 Estimates of Reserves Extensions

4.4.1 Extensions

Reserves and additions to productive capacity come from both extensions and discoveries. Extensions include wells drilled which increase reserves or rates of production on previously discovered fields. Extensions can be classed into two categories, infill and edge. Infill wells are generally wells drilled below the normal well spacing of an area in order to tap oil residing between two existing wells which would otherwise be unrecoverable. Edge wells are drilled on the extremities of a particular pool in order to expand or increase the size of a particular pool. Both types of wells are usually termed development wells.

4.4.2 Estimating Reserves From Extensions

The methodology employed in this model requires that an initial production rate be provided for every well. Given the initial production rate, a decline rate is applied according to the region within which the well is located. The Saskatchewan Activity Model provides an estimate of successful development wells. These wells are classified either as wells associated with older fields or wells required by new discoveries.

4.4.3 New Discovery Extensions

The results of the discovery model provide the number and size of newly discovered pools. This information includes the play category from which average play characteristics can be implied. These average play characteristics allow an areal extent of each pool to be calculated.[13] If normal well spacing assumptions are applied, the number of successful extension wells can be calculated. After the number of wells is determined, the average production over time and ultimate recovery of the pool will imply an initial production rate for each well in that pool. The development wells are then designated to be drilled over a 3-year period.

4.4.4 Old Pool Extensions

To generate an estimate of old pool extension wells, new pool extensions are subtracted from the total successful development wells. Calculating the initial production rates for these wells is not as simple. Since the extension wells increase the size of older pools, the pool size cannot be used as a guide. History, however, seems to demonstrate that the initial production rates of wells in Saskatchewan do not show a significant decline; therefore the average initial production rate for each area could be used. A range of production rates will likely be obtained from these extensions. Ten different rates for each area were used. In this way, initial production rates will simulate the range of success experienced by different extension prospects.

4.4.5 Declining Initial Production Rates

The question of whether initial production rates should decline within the modelling system has generated considerable discussion. There are two major factors which are likely to have influence over the average initial production rates of new wells in Saskatchewan. The number of wells drilled as new discoveries relative to the number of wells drilled as extensions of old pools will affect the average initial production rate of new wells drilled in the province. Since extensions form a large part of the new drilling, initial production rates, on average, are predicted to fall one-half of one percent on a declining balance basis within each producing area. This amounts approximately to a .05 percent decline in the initial production rate per well drilled in each of the six areas. This is intended to reduce the reserves which will be added due to extensions and infill drilling as the Saskatchewan Basin matures.

4.4.6 Water Production

An important determinant in the productivity of a particular well is the volume of water production. In order to select ranges for water production, three different levels of water production were selected for each region. New wells were assigned water production rates according to the historical percentage of wells in each category in each region. Therefore, a high productivity well may receive a high or low water cut allocation depending upon the region and a random selection process. Given these assumptions, the distribution of water levels will approximate the average for each area over time.

4.4.7 Royalty Status

A royalty and tax status was assigned to each new well. New wells are currently exempt from royalties for a period of time depending on their classification. Once they become non-exempt they are classified as either freehold or Crown according to historical averages in each area. Using this random average percentage method, all classes will eventually approximate historical averages from each area. All extension wells will therefore produce according to historical patterns. These patterns can be adapted to reflect changes if additional area specific information becomes available.

4.4.8 Volume of Extension Additions

The volume of extensions over time is determined by the number of successful extension wells drilled and by the initial production rates of those wells. These parameters can also be easily changed to reflect additional information on success rates and production profiles.

4.5 Modelling the System

4.5.1 Choosing Beta and Monte Carlo Results

The value of Beta was assumed to equal one (B = 1) in our analysis. The model does contain the flexibility to run Beta values which are different from one. A base case using B = 1 assumes that pools will be discovered with a probability proportional to their pool size.

One run per case was performed. A more thorough analysis would entail the running of additional estimates, randomly choosing different pool sizes. This procedure, known as Monte Carlo simulation, would yield a range of likely discoveries instead of a point estimate in each year.

4.5.2 The Model

The entire model consists of two major sections, the short-run and the long-run. The short-run section needs to be run only once for each price/economic set of assumptions. The long-run section may be run many times under different random pool selections in order to obtain a Monte Carlo distribution. The results below (section 4.6) are

examples of one run of both the short-run and long-run results. The
flow chart for the reserves additions is presented in Figure 4.2.

4.6 Results

In Figure 4.3, long-run production over time is presented for
the three different price scenarios. The low case shows a leveling
out at around one-half current production. The base case shows a
decline and then an increase as higher prices expected in the future
encourage additional drilling. The high case shows a large response to
very attractive economic conditions. Tables 4.1, 4.2, and 4.3 show the
model results from the long-run supply scenarios.

Figure 4.4 shows a comparison between the short-run supply
curve and the long-run supply curve. Table 4.4 shows the differences
in elasticities between the two curves. In Chapter 6 the additions are
broken down into new pool additions and additions from extensions to
existing pools.

TABLE 4.4

ELASTICITIES OF SUPPLY

Price Change $Cdn./bbl	$10/$20	$20/$30
Short-run	0.204	0.081
Long-run	0.778	0.390

SOURCE: Canadian Energy Research Institute.

The response of supply to price changes within the ranges
recently experienced can cause large shifts in the ultimate supply of
oil from Saskatchewan. The high elasticities for the long-run supply
show that continued weakness in oil prices could severely inhibit
Saskatchewan's productive capacity. Prices above $30 may not have
large effects on short-run supply, but the additions potential,
although tempered by the physical limits of the resource, retains a
long-run elasticity as high as 0.390.

Given the change in elasticity over a range of prices, it may
be worthwhile to run further scenarios to test lower and higher price
ranges. It becomes clear that one elasticity value is not sufficient
to measure the response of supply over various price scenarios.

38

FIGURE 4.2   SASKATCHEWAN SUPPLY CURVE
DISCOVERY MODEL.

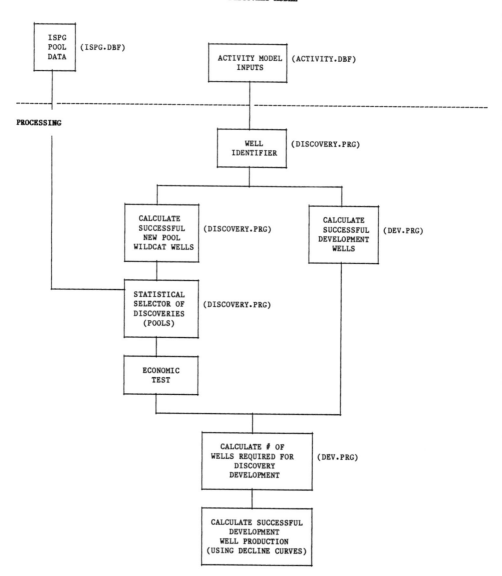

SOURCE: Canadian Energy Research Institute.

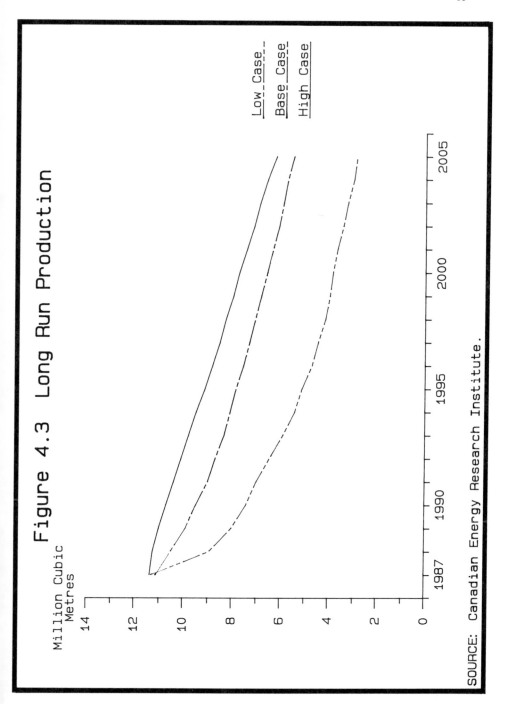

Figure 4.3 Long Run Production

Million Cubic Metres

Low Case

Base Case

High Case

SOURCE: Canadian Energy Research Institute.

TABLE 4.1

LONG-RUN SUPPLY
LOW CASE
(cubic metres)

Year	Area 1 Totals	Area 2 Totals	Area 3 Totals	Area 4 Totals	Area 5 Totals	Area 6 Totals	Total of Totals
1986	2 974 555	804 318	1 866 295	2 241 174	1 219 914	2 902 586	12 008 843
1987	2 491 757	754 144	1 728 658	2 269 423	1 166 196	2 904 322	11 314 501
1988	1 619 505	610 345	1 489 675	1 844 594	1 002 053	2 383 020	8 949 193
1989	1 328 685	549 630	1 334 703	1 753 380	923 171	2 179 214	8 068 783
1990	1 128 096	519 460	1 196 685	1 698 388	868 284	2 030 057	7 440 971
1991	1 047 417	485 179	1 070 807	1 666 915	821 639	1 926 919	7 018 876
1992	941 661	439 216	960 123	1 577 883	756 740	1 772 352	6 447 977
1993	788 168	419 111	859 025	1 517 892	703 750	1 626 947	5 914 892
1994	667 287	377 780	765 273	1 446 540	654 246	1 506 320	5 417 445
1995	555 051	356 895	687 051	1 445 951	614 004	1 445 751	5 104 702
1996	464 057	331 073	613 648	1 390 335	562 269	1 368 236	4 729 617
1997	396 877	295 149	602 147	1 366 029	517 309	1 272 853	4 450 364
1998	329 670	267 585	539 481	1 312 224	477 799	1 207 826	4 134 584
1999	280 620	239 403	489 486	1 297 580	444 413	1 214 742	3 966 244
2000	339 804	215 598	441 985	1 247 353	421 107	1 185 056	3 850 904
2001	288 607	194 330	434 213	1 223 738	395 583	1 148 479	3 684 950
2002	244 659	172 740	393 964	1 180 498	370 729	1 074 353	3 436 943
2003	203 748	152 963	360 032	1 171 302	343 696	996 727	3 228 467
2004	198 424	137 654	329 939	1 134 637	316 791	900 009	3 017 455
2005	163 379	119 451	315 761	1 122 521	296 193	885 131	2 902 435
Totals	16 452 028	7 442 022	16 478 950	29 908 355	12 875 890	31 930 901	115 088 146

SOURCE: Canadian Energy Research Institute.

TABLE 4.2

LONG-RUN SUPPLY
BASE CASE
(cubic metres)

Year	Area 1 Totals	Area 2 Totals	Area 3 Totals	Area 4 Totals	Area 5 Totals	Area 6 Totals	Total of Totals
1986	2 974 555	804 318	1 866 295	2 241 174	1 219 914	2 902 586	12 008 843
1987	2 509 149	757 381	1 701 147	2 224 518	1 178 928	2 737 775	11 108 898
1988	2 292 154	726 313	1 561 912	2 194 129	1 126 797	2 590 289	10 491 594
1989	2 061 069	692 053	1 459 862	2 162 096	1 072 327	2 484 920	9 932 328
1990	1 901 707	668 650	1 346 204	2 137 528	1 030 341	2 399 076	9 483 507
1991	1 705 921	651 684	1 252 349	2 115 048	982 336	2 316 392	9 023 730
1992	1 621 238	636 487	1 162 592	2 088 930	941 762	2 229 436	8 680 445
1993	1 482 332	626 170	1 088 491	2 060 508	918 167	2 136 358	8 312 026
1994	1 399 144	626 665	1 020 833	2 034 220	887 635	2 120 759	8 089 306
1995	1 309 740	627 236	959 001	2 009 324	861 396	2 077 265	7 843 962
1996	1 195 508	625 234	909 035	1 971 487	829 944	2 034 143	7 565 441
1997	1 125 560	626 816	861 416	1 950 201	811 172	1 958 915	7 334 080
1998	1 039 567	624 247	822 851	1 914 312	784 787	1 869 568	7 055 332
1999	957 017	633 677	792 289	1 895 530	769 119	1 791 834	6 839 466
2000	856 158	629 828	759 483	1 868 125	739 680	1 704 324	6 557 598
2001	785 780	621 719	745 050	1 840 238	720 825	1 618 203	6 331 814
2002	704 277	616 159	720 372	1 798 656	706 582	1 533 704	6 079 749
2003	646 974	610 322	699 791	1 769 149	696 115	1 486 701	5 909 051
2004	570 105	614 630	690 343	1 737 932	674 125	1 420 675	5 707 810
2005	517 377	608 023	677 889	1 696 196	649 470	1 355 046	5 504 001
Totals	27 655 331	13 027 701	21 097 255	39 709 299	17 601 423	40 767 970	159 858 979

SOURCE: Canadian Energy Research Institute.

TABLE 4.3

LONG-RUN SUPPLY
HIGH CASE
(cubic metres)

Year	Area 1 Totals	Area 2 Totals	Area 3 Totals	Area 4 Totals	Area 5 Totals	Area 6 Totals	Total of Totals
1986	2 974 555	804 318	1 866 295	2 241 174	1 219 914	2 902 586	12 008 843
1987	2 505 020	751 043	1 746 551	2 275 594	1 192 356	2 905 201	11 375 766
1988	2 437 250	750 448	1 642 218	2 347 792	1 146 254	2 948 122	11 272 084
1989	2 253 792	767 587	1 543 016	2 390 752	1 107 538	2 949 541	11 012 226
1990	2 124 979	787 976	1 452 523	2 407 798	1 066 115	2 870 863	10 710 254
1991	1 953 745	815 440	1 369 464	2 421 452	1 033 647	2 805 301	10 399 048
1992	1 841 675	806 699	1 308 523	2 416 060	998 135	2 739 576	10 110 669
1993	1 709 604	809 692	1 237 222	2 395 367	974 077	2 661 642	9 787 603
1994	1 594 673	806 067	1 185 643	2 367 497	943 371	2 564 228	9 461 479
1995	1 486 759	816 207	1 130 470	2 346 683	916 414	2 445 682	9 142 215
1996	1 368 939	826 332	1 088 291	2 313 513	895 131	2 332 986	8 825 192
1997	1 283 400	833 199	1 052 547	2 283 593	881 587	2 214 153	8 548 477
1998	1 186 362	843 419	1 014 951	2 246 986	862 235	2 100 836	8 254 789
1999	1 098 244	850 150	990 303	2 197 938	838 458	1 984 972	7 960 064
2000	1 008 433	867 940	965 625	2 157 507	817 545	1 886 887	7 703 936
2001	926 108	868 254	942 416	2 106 487	809 193	1 773 106	7 425 563
2002	843 498	872 473	923 766	2 050 064	793 889	1 654 161	7 138 751
2003	775 281	872 574	911 448	1 995 483	774 602	1 533 584	6 862 972
2004	699 303	883 620	897 205	1 932 889	747 234	1 394 134	6 554 386
2005	632 544	878 233	883 795	1 872 710	723 042	1 250 423	6 240 747
Totals	30 704 166	16 511 672	24 152 270	44 768 238	18 740 735	45 917 983	180 795 064

SOURCE: Canadian Energy Research Institute.

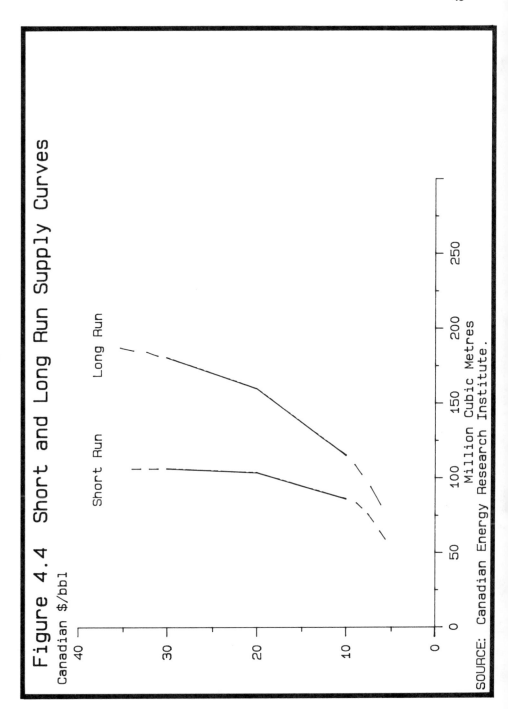

Figure 4.4 Short and Long Run Supply Curves

Canadian $/bbl

SOURCE: Canadian Energy Research Institute.

Footnotes

[1]B. Scarfe and E. Rilkoff, Financing Oil and Gas Exploration and Development Activity Discussion Paper No. 274, (Ottawa: Economic Council of Canada, December 1984).

[2]S. Madduri and J. N. Tanner, "A Petroleum Activity Model," Alberta Energy and Natural Resources Working Paper 1983 (Edmonton: September 1983).

[3]Peter C. Bing and John Gillies, "A Model of Exploration Drilling Activity," paper presented to the Ninth International Conference of the International Association of Energy Economists in Calgary, July 1987.

[4]Supra, footnote 2.

[5]Abha Bhargava, Effects of Public Policy on the Supply of Petroleum in Alberta, Ph.D. Thesis, University of Alberta, 1986.

[6]Abha Bhargava, "Saskatchewan Disaggregated Drilling Model," paper prepared for Saskatchewan Department of Energy and Mines, 1987.

[7]John Lohrenz, "The Supply of Oil and Gas From Basins: Lessons from History," paper presented to the Ninth International Conference of the International Association of Energy Economists in Calgary, July 1987.

[8]Kenneth D. Foat and Alan J. MacFadyen, Modelling Exploration Success in Alberta Oil Plays, Study No. 19 (Calgary: Canadian Energy Research Institute, September 1983).

[9]Ibid.

[10]E. Barouch and G. M. Kaufman, "Sampling Without Replacement and Proportional to Random Size," Unpublished Manuscripts, 1974.

[11]P. J. Lee and P. C. C. Wang, "Prediction of Oil or Gas Pool Sizes When Discovery Record is Available," Journal of Mathematical Geology, Vol. 17, No. 2 (1985).

[12]Malcolm Wilson and R. W. Bennett "Evaluation of Saskatchewan's Heavy Oil Reserves," report prepared for Saskatchewan Department of Energy and Mines, 1985.

[13]These calculations are provided in Appendix F.

Chapter 5

THE ACTIVITY MODEL SPECIFICATIONS*

5.1 Saskatchewan Disaggregated
Activity Model

5.1.1 Introduction

In this chapter, we present a description of the Saskatchewan Disaggregated Activity Model and empirical results. This model was formulated for policy analysis and is effective in analyzing the impact of past policies on levels of activity in the Saskatchewan petroleum industry and also the impact of future policy proposals. This model was included in this study because it was appropriately disaggregated and allowed for the integration of the technical work of geologists, engineers, and economists. This model was created using econometric techniques. It estimates future drilling in Saskatchewan based upon predictions of oil and gas prices and other factors described below.

The Saskatchewan Disaggregated Activity Model is similar in format to the Saskatchewan Aggregated Activity Model[1] with the exception that the former only estimates well activity while the latter estimates well activity, production and reserves additions. Although both models are ad hoc specifications of behavioural relationships evident in the oil and gas industry, the Saskatchewan Aggregated Activity Model is a simplified version of a more rigorous model formulated for the Alberta oil and gas industry.[2] The parent model is a micro, partial equilibrium model in which an oil and gas firm maximizes the present value of a stream of future anticipated profits subject to a Constant Elasticity of Transformation (CET) function and two capital flow constraints.

---

*Dr. Abha Bhargava of the Saskatchewan Department of Energy and Mines wrote part of, and provided considerable input to, the material contained in this Chapter.

5.1.2 Model Specification

A single log-linear behavioural equation explaining well drilling is specified and then estimated. The equation is as follows:

$$\text{LOG WELL} = A_0 + A_1 \text{ LOG NET} + A_2 \text{ LOG COST} + A_3 \text{ LOG SU} + A_4 \text{ LOG EXP} + A_5 \text{ LOG PGAS} + A_6 \text{ DUF} + A_7 \text{ DUP}$$

Where

WELL = total number of oil wells drilled in period t
NET = netback per barrel in period t
COST = drilling cost per well in period t
SU   = weighted average success ratio in period t
EXP = weighted average expected profitability in period t
DUF = dummy variable to capture the negative policy effects
DUP = dummy variable to capture the positive policy effects
PGAS = wellhead price of gas per cubic metre net of royalties
       in period t

In the above equation, the netback (NET) is calculated as wellhead price of oil minus royalties and operating costs. Similarly,
drilling costs (COST) are calculated net of federal tax incentives such
as the cumulative exploration expenditure write-off allowance, investment tax credit, Canadian oil and gas property expense allowance,
depletion allowance and PIP grants.[3] The inclusion of royalties and
the various tax incentives through these two variables introduces
parameters of critical interest to policy makers. These parameters can
be easily manipulated in this model to study their effect on investment
in the oil and gas industry.

Success ratio (SU) in the above equation is a weighted average
of the current and past year's success ratio. Geological success can
be as important as economic considerations in determining investment.
This variable can be measured either as a ratio of successful wells to
total wells drilled or as a ratio of reserves generated to successful
wells drilled. Theoretically, it is the amount of reserves discovered
that is of importance to the operator, rather than the number of
successful wells. A well may be successful but the size of the discovery may be too small to be economic. Reserves additions are significantly volatile and may vary from zero additions in any one year to
significant discoveries in the next. Although large discoveries prompt
a burst of activity, the impact on drilling is more distributed over
time. Unless the discoveries are averaged, the extreme volatility
presents a problem in estimation. Both measures of success were

estimated but only the ratio of successful to total wells drilled was included in the final estimation.

EXP, the weighted average expected profitability, is measured by bonus bids paid per acre in a given geological region in time period t . In making a bid, the investor is concerned primarily with two factors: first, the discovery prospects on that tract which can be represented by an expected success ratio and second, the financial return from that tract.

Both success ratio and expected profitability are measured as weighted averages of the two most recent annual actual values. While current values may be an accurate reflection of producer's expectations of the variables in question, we hypothesize that it is more likely that the expectations are based on the observed pattern of values over several years. The weights used in the calculation of both success ratios and expected profitability differ between the various areas.

The price of gas (PGAS) is also calculated net of gas royalties. Since there is no significant drilling for gas in areas other than Area 3, price of gas is included as an explanatory variable only in this area.

Two dummy variables, DUF and DUP were included in the model to capture the direct effect of government policies. DUF captured the negative policy effect. DUF = 1 for years in which Bill 42[4] and the National Energy Program were in effect (i.e., 1974 - 1977; 1981 - 1984). DUF = 0 for the remaining years. DUP captured the positive policy effects. It equaled 1 for years in which the royalty holidays were in effect (1982, 1983, 1984) and 0 for remaining years.

5.1.3 Exploration and Development

Note that in this model no distinction is made between the exploration and development phase. Both types of activity are grouped in the one variable--the number of wells drilled. Theoretically, exploration and development are two different phases of investment in the oil and gas industry. Exploration involves activities directed towards finding oil and gas and consists of geological or geophysical techniques and exploratory drilling. It is an information-generating process whereby the information generated either substantiates or negates the presence of oil or gas. Development, on the other hand, entails the establishment of productive capacity including additional drilling and installation of facilities for the extraction of crude oil. In practice, both exploration and development aim at establishing the size of the reserves base. But because exploration involves wildcatting and occurs in generally unknown areas, the risk in exploration is substantially greater than in development.

The Saskatchewan Disaggregated Model does not distinguish between the two phases largely because of a relatively small sample size. This model takes into account the six production areas which are classified according to the various qualities of oil (light, medium, and heavy) and the geological characteristics. Given the small size of the Saskatchewan oil and gas industry, its classification into six areas and further sub-classification into exploration and development would render very small observations of the dependent variable and hence make empirical estimation less reliable.

5.1.4 Data

The model is estimated for the years 1969 to 1984 for the six producing areas in the province. For the purposes of oil production, the province of Saskatchewan is divided into six production areas by type of oil and geological formation. The six areas are as follows:

Area 1 - Lloydminster Heavy
Area 2 - Kindersley/Kerrobert Heavy
Area 3 - Swift Curent Medium
Area 4 - Weyburn/Estevan Medium
Area 5 - Kindersley/Kerrobert Light
Area 6 - Weyburn/Estevan Light

The price of oil, the cost of production, productivity and success ratios vary significantly among these areas. All the data used in the model were obtained from the internal files of the Saskatchewan Department of Energy and Mines.

5.1.5 Results

The model was estimated using Ordinary Least Squares (OLS). The results for the six areas are provided in Table 5.1. Most estimated coefficients of explanatory variables are highly significant and the equations have a good fit. The Durbin-Watson statistics evidence no serial correlation of the residuals. The magnitude of elasticities and the level of significance differs between areas. Note that the drilling cost was found to be significant only for Area 1 and Area 6,

TABLE 5.1

REGRESSION COEFFICIENTS[a]

	(A_0)	NET (A_1)	COST (A_2)	SU (A_3)	EXP (A_4)	PGAS (A_5)	DUF (A_6)	DUP (A_7)	R^2	$\bar{R}^2$	D.W.	df
Area 1	7.51 (5.02)[b]	0.95 (2.57)[b]	-0.60 (-1.89)[b]	6.11 (2.28)[b]	0.26 (4.55)[b]	—	-0.33 (-1.74)	-1.28 (-1.75)[c]	0.93	0.88	1.79	8
Area 2	-0.09 (-0.06)	1.70 (3.08)[b]	—	2.86 (2.55)[b]	-0.17 (-0.53)	—	0.04 (0.05)	-2.42 (-2.43)[b]	0.86	0.78	1.98	9
Area 3	1.14 (1.32)	0.67 (2.68)[b]	—	—	0.43 (1.46)[c]	—	-2.37 (-4.25)[b]	1.05 (1.41)[c]	0.77	0.67	1.85	10
Area 4	1.77 (3.22)[b]	0.45 (1.85)[b]	—	—	0.24 (2.31)[b]	-0.13 (-0.41)	-1.04 (-3.73)[b]	1.12 (3.88)[b]	0.91	0.87	1.76	10
Area 5	2.20 (6.82)[b]	0.34 (3.64)[b]	—	0.65 (2.57)[b]	0.46 (6.23)[b]	—	-1.11 (-8.85)[b]	0.98 (7.22)[b]	0.99	0.99	2.31	9
Area 6	2.80 (3.13)[b]	0.49 (1.66)[c]	-0.26 (-1.28)	—	0.46 (4.18)[b]	—	-0.53 (-1.87)[c]	0.63 (2.27)[b]	0.93	0.88	2.47	9

SOURCE: Saskatchewan Energy and Mines.

[a]The t-statistics are given in parenthesis.
[b]Indicates that the variable is significant at 0.95 level of significance.
[c]Indicates that the variable is significant at 0.90 level of significance.
—Indicates that the variable was not included in the final estimating equation because it was insignificant.

hence, this variable was eliminated in the final equations for the remaining areas.

The netback is uniformly significant in all equations. Since royalties are included in the calculation of netback, it indicates the importance of royalties as a policy tool. The netback has a higher elasticity in the two heavy oil areas, which are the costliest in terms of drilling and operating costs. Also, these areas have a higher proportion of marginal wells whose existence may be more sensitive to financial return. Expected profitability is statistically significant in all but one area. The two dummy variables are relatively more significant in the light oil areas. Note that both Kindersley-light and Estevan-light areas responded strongly to the royalty holiday program.

5.1.6 Conclusions and Policy Implications

The results indicate that public policy has a significant impact on investment in the oil and gas sector, although this effect varies between areas. The elasticity of well activity with respect to netback varies from a high of 1.70 and .95 in Areas 2 and 1, respectively, to a low of .34 for Area 5. DUP, which incorporates the royalty holiday program introduced in 1983, also has a varying elasticity for different areas.

An insignificant drilling cost variable indicates that the effect of any policy that directly influences costs will be negligible. Thus the effect of depletion allowance, or the various federal tax concessions, may be minimal. This result is similar to that obtained for the Alberta oil and gas industry. Note that the drilling costs increased tremendously in much of the estimation period. The drilling cost per well increased over four fold from $55,000 in 1969 to $235,000 in 1984. While drilling activity fluctuated in some years, in general it increased from 1,191 wells in 1969 to 2,970 wells in 1984, an increase of 149 percent. The results both in Saskatchewan and Alberta may be capturing a supply effect, i.e., an increase in demand for drilling inputs would lead to an increase in drilling cost. Thus, instead of a change in drilling cost leading to a change in activity, a reverse causality may be more pronounced.

The effect of expected profitability on well drilling is pronounced in all areas except Areas 2 and 3. That this variable would be significant is hardly surprising. Expectations play a key role in this world of uncertainty. Prices and geological success are the main factors creating uncertainty.

In general, the results obtained from the Saskatchewan model are quite similar to those obtained from the Alberta supply model. Although the exact magnitude of elasticities may not be directly comparable because of a different specification, the following can still be noted. The price of oil and market expectations are significant determinants of activity. Cost variables are not as significant.

5.2 Discovery Model

5.2.1 Successful Wells

The discovery model uses the Institute of Sedimentary and Petroleum Geology data base of undiscovered pools, which is comprised of the pool sizes remaining to be discovered classified into play categories. The goal of the discovery model is to select pools which will be discovered in each year. We noted that success ratios tend to be fairly constant over time.[5] If the volume of exploration drilling is properly forecast, a new pool success ratio applied to that activity will forecast the number of new pools discovered in each region each year. Table 5.2 contains the success ratios which were used. The remaining requirement for the discovery model is to forecast the size of each of these pools.

TABLE 5.2

SUCCESS RATIOS BY AREA

	Area 1	Area 2	Area 3	Area 4	Area 5	Area 6
Exploration	.1410	.1113	.1166	.1300	.1113	.0850
Development	.8033	.7689	.6700	.7511	.7689	.7511

SOURCE: Canadian Energy Research Institute.

5.2.2 Size of Pools

Given the "sampling without replacement" methodology, new pool discoveries will be made proportionate to pool size. The program takes each successful well from each area and randomly chooses a pool from the pools remaining to be discovered in that area. The Kaufman formula was used with Beta set consistently equal to one.[6] This process is repeated for each successful well. Because this is a random sampling method, each separate run will likely have different discovery sequences. The analysis is therefore amenable to the use of Monte Carlo simulation technologies, although these have not been employed for the purposes of this study.

Once a pool is chosen, it is eliminated from the undiscovered category. Each pool is classified into a play category defined for a certain set of average play characteristics.

5.2.3 Play Characteristics

In order to analyze the economics of any particular pool, additional information is required concerning the likely areal extent of the pool, the depth, and the recovery of oil from the reservoir. Since each pool size is assigned a play category, we chose to use average recovery factors, average formation volume factors, and average depth factors taken from existing plays in Saskatchewan.

The areal extent calculation involved estimating a relationship between the pool sizes and the areal extent of a pool. This was required in order to determine the number of wells to be drilled in the pool. The estimate of the relationships between the size and the areal extent of the pool was made for each separate play by approximating a log normal relationship between the two variables.[7] Once the areal extent was calculated, the number of wells was calculated using the normal spacing requirements for each area. An average production rate was then assigned to each well by dividing the estimated production evenly among the number of wells in the pool. The wells were allowed to produce over a 20-year period to recover all the oil reserves assigned at a decline rate which was average for the area. The production scenario was then calculated and the initial production rate of each well was extracted from the production profiles. A copy of the pool-by-pool data base averages used for the averaging calculations is included in Table 5.3.[8]

TABLE 5.3

AVERAGE PLAY CHARACTERISTICS

Play[a]	Assigned Area	Averages					
		Primary Recovery (percent)	Net Pay (metres)	Average Porosity	Water Saturation	Formation Volume	Average Depth (metres)
Rex, Lloydminster; Cummings	1	4.42	6.27	32.0	27.6	1.056	617
General Petroleums	1	5.03	4.93	33.9	25.4	1.041	507
Colony, McLaren Waseca	1	5.79	4.56	32.9	21.7	1.045	486
Sparky	1	5.19	4.85	33.2	21.3	1.043	546
Bakken	2	4.71	7.46	28.5	24.4	1.063	817
Basal Mannville	3	5.02	5.12	23.9	39.5	1.098	1002
Roseray Success	3	9.86	4.84	26.1	30.3	1.059	966
Upper Shaunavon	3	8.91	3.65	16.9	25.6	1.068	1286
Alida Frobisher	4	18.89	7.30	11.2	38.8	1.190	1284
Midale Beds	4	12.26	4.96	15.8	37.7	1.137	1428
Ratcliffe Structural	4	12.23	5.52	16.3	40.5	1.193	1876
Viking Sand	5	7.32	2.78	22.9	42.7	1.101	698
Upper Devonian	6	16.07	7.07	12.3	31.4	1.204	1622
Ratcliffe Stratigraphic	6	8.90	6.76	13.6	39.0	1.232	1885
Souris Valley Tilston	6	16.41	8.91	12.4	41.4	1.117	1106

SOURCE: Canadian Energy Research Institute.

[a]The new Winipegosis play has not been included because of lack of data.

54

These play characteristics were used in the model in order to calculate the likely production rates of each new pool discovered. Well spacing was also an important factor. The well spacing used in each area is presented in Table 5.4.

TABLE 5.4

WELL SPACING BY AREA

Area	Well Spacing (square metres)	LSD
1	162 000	1
2	162 000	1
3	486 000	2 or 4
4	324 000	2
5	162 000	1
6	324 000	2

SOURCE: Canadian Energy Research Institute.

5.2.4 Development

The second source of reserves additions in the model comes from development of existing pools. To isolate this factor, the forecast of development wells was reduced by the development wells drilled as a result of new discoveries. The remaining wells in each area were randomly assigned one of ten different initial production rates, which averaged to the average initial production rate for that area. In this way a full range of development successes was added to the data base. The average initial production rates are provided in Table 5.5.

TABLE 5.5

INITIAL PRODUCTION RATES
OF DEVELOPMENT WELLS
(cubic metres/month)

Area 1	Area 2	Area 3	Area 4	Area 5	Area 6
43	47	107	78	7	52
53	57	117	88	17	62
63	67	127	98	27	72
73	77	137	108	37	82
83	87	147	118	47	92
93	97	157	128	57	102
103	107	167	138	67	112
113	117	177	148	77	122
123	127	187	158	87	132
133	137	197	168	97	142
Average					
88	92	152	123	52	97

SOURCE: Canadian Energy Research Institute.

NOTE: Each column represents a range of production rates used in each area.

These initial production rates were then declined by 1 percent per well on a declining balance basis. This means that the first well received the initial production rate presented above. The second well assigned to that production rate would produce at 99 percent of that amount. The third, assigned to that production category, would produce at 98.01 percent of that amount.

Footnotes

[1]Abha Bhargava, "Saskatchewan Aggregated Activity Model," report prepared for internal use of Saskatchewan Energy and Mines, 1985.

[2]Abha Bhargava, Effects of Public Policy on the Supply of Petroleum in Alberta, Ph.D. Thesis, University of Alberta, 1986.

[3]For exact formulation of the cost equations, the reader is referred to Bhargava (1986), p. 210-212.

[4]The Oil and Gas Conservation, Stabilization and Development Act was repealed in 1974 under Bill 42. This bill imposed a mineral income tax on oil and gas revenue and effected the expropriation of all oil and gas rights in the producing tracts within the province for some compensation. The introduction of this legislation caused a furor in the oil and gas industry and led to a challenge of the legislation in the courts. However, the Supreme Court did uphold the powers of the province to acquire the oil and gas rights in a producing tract.

[5]John Lohrenz, "The Supply of Oil and Gas From Basins: Lessons from History," paper presented to the Ninth International Conference of the International Association of Energy Economists, held in Calgary, July 1987.

[6]Chapter 4, Section 4.3.4 refers to B=1 in this equation.

[7]The estimate was made by approximating the coefficient "a" in the equation: ln(Pool Size) = a ln(Areal Extent). This method is similar to a method used by Energy, Mines and Resources Canada in a similar modelling system.

[8]This type of methodology was used in a study by Energy, Mines and Resources Canada entitled, Conventional Oil Resources of Western Canada (Light and Medium), Part II, Economic Analysis, Paper 87-26, by R. F. Conn, and J. A. Christie.

Chapter 6

ANALYSIS OF ADDITIONS

6.1 Short-Term Additions Versus
     Short-Run Supply

In order to understand the complexities of oil supply, it was necessary to divide the analysis into short- and long-run categories. However, for policy initiatives, governments and supply planners are likely to be interested in several additional categories.

A dramatic change in prices for a short period of time could produce a short-term supply response. This is different from what we define as short-run. Short-term supply is a subset of the long-run supply analysis. To generate an analysis of short-term effects one would simply generate different scenarios of long-run supply.

The short-term response must be defined by specifying a time period. How much additional oil could be discovered in a 3-year period if the price was to increase by $10 per barrel? Referring to our long-run files we can determine the difference between the number of wells added in the two cases, decline those wells over time, and generate the short-term increase in oil supply. These increases would generally be much smaller than the long-run elasticities in Chapter 4 simply because they encompass only 3 years of additions, while the total elasticities of Chapter 4 include 19 years of additions.

6.2 Elasticities Will Change As
     Depletion Occurs

As an exhaustible resource is depleted, less reserve is available to be recovered; therefore, the percentage of remaining reserves will change as production takes place. The elasticity, which is percentage change in reserves due to percentage change in price, will therefore change as the reserves are depleted.

Higher supply costs associated with more remote and/or partially depleted volumes of oil will raise the relevant hurdle price and the marginal shut-in rates. The price will therefore have to increase at a higher rate to obtain the same reserves response. Therefore, not only does the finite reserve decline but the cost of the remaining reserve increases, often at a variable rate.

The range of possible elasticities re-emphasizes the importance of establishing clear definitions of short- and long-run supply. Otherwise, estimates of isolated changes in supply and their elasticities cannont be compared.

6.3 The Structure of Additions

Additions come from two basic sources in our modelling system. The first source is additions from new discoveries and the associated development of new discoveries. The second source is extensions to existing pools. If future supply sources are divided into reserves associated with new discoveries and reserves associated with existing pools, a better understanding can be obtained of Saskatchewan's ultimate potential.

Additions from exploration and associated development are represented separately from additions from extensions and infill drilling in Tables 6.1, 6.2, and 6.3. These tables represent the low case, base case, and high case, respectively. The relative size of probable additions from exploration is small. This is an important factor in Saskatchewan oil supply. This relationship is shown in Figures 6.1 and 6.2. Notice that the additions from exploration, represented by the area between the first and second curves in Figure 6.1, do not shift the supply curve dramatically to the right, whereas the extensions curve represented by the difference between the new pools curve and the long-run supply curve shifts the supply curve significantly.

In a recent presentation to the U.S. House of Representatives, William L. Fisher presented statistics on the sources of U.S. reserves additions during the period 1976 to 1985.[1] He found that fifteen percent (15%) of additions came from new field discoveries and five percent (5%) from new pools. The remaining eighty percent (80%) came from reserves growth such as infill (55%), extensions (20%), and EOR (5%).

If we compare our forecasts with these numbers we find the percentage of our additions coming from new pools is as follows: Low Case, 19.30 percent; Base Case, 18.67 percent, and High Case, 21.01 percent. Fisher's percentages included EOR; since we have not included

TABLE 6.1

SASKATCHEWAN OIL SUPPLY SUMMARY
LOW CASE
(cubic metres)

Totals For	Area 1	Area 2	Area 3	Area 4	Area 5	Area 6	Total
Short Run	14 792 034	6 513 368	14 657 618	19 283 586	9 371 673	21 503 449	86 121 726
New Pool Additions	610 184	209 501	208 706	552 112	896 859	3 043 691	5 593 053
Old Pool Additions	1 049 810	719 153	1 540 626	10 072 657	2 607 358	7 383 761	23 373 365
Totals	16 452 028	7 442 022	16 478 950	29 908 355	12 875 890	31 930 901	115 088 144

SOURCE: Canadian Energy Research Institute.

TABLE 6.2

SASKATCHEWAN OIL SUPPLY SUMMARY
BASE CASE
(cubic metres)

Totals For	Area 1	Area 2	Area 3	Area 4	Area 5	Area 6	Total
Short Run	20 658 042	7 590 715	16 003 733	23 175 695	10 759 625	25 480 087	103 667 895
New Pool Additions	1 738 265	928 496	295 263	1 917 546	1 948 506	3 663 605	10 491 682
Old Pool Additions	5 259 024	4 508 490	4 798 260	14 616 058	4 893 292	11 624 277	45 699 402
Totals	27 655 331	13 027 701	21 097 256	39 709 299	17 601 423	40 767 969	159 858 979

SOURCE: Canadian Energy Research Institute.

TABLE 6.3

SASKATCHEWAN OIL SUPPLY SUMMARY
HIGH CASE
(cubic metres)

Totals For	Area 1	Area 2	Area 3	Area 4	Area 5	Area 6	Total
Short Run	21 886 508	7 733 196	16 099 671	23 587 819	10 918 576	26 245 104	106 470 874
New Pool Additions	2 841 142	2 091 243	629 151	2 651 395	2 315 167	5 091 269	15 619 368
Old Pool Additions	5 976 517	6 687 232	7 423 448	18 529 024	5 506 993	14 581 608	58 704 821
Totals	30 704 167	16 511 671	24 152 270	44 768 238	18 740 736	45 917 981	180 795 063

SOURCE: Canadian Energy Research Institute.

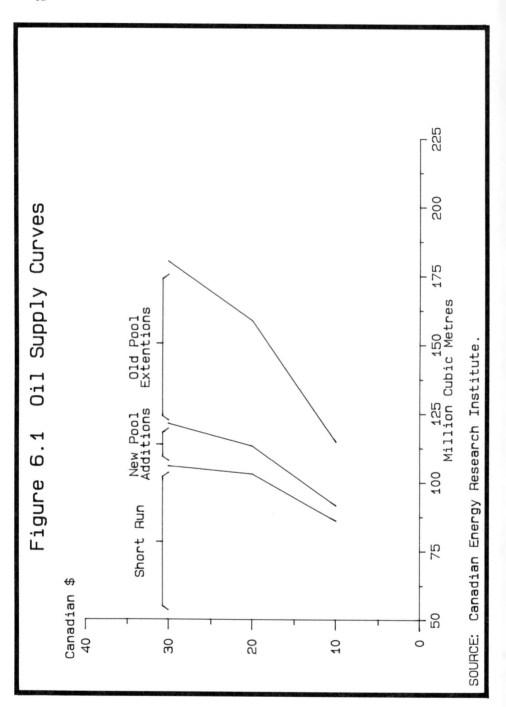

Figure 6.1 Oil Supply Curves

Canadian $

Short Run   New Pool Additions   Old Pool Extentions

Million Cubic Metres

SOURCE: Canadian Energy Research Institute.

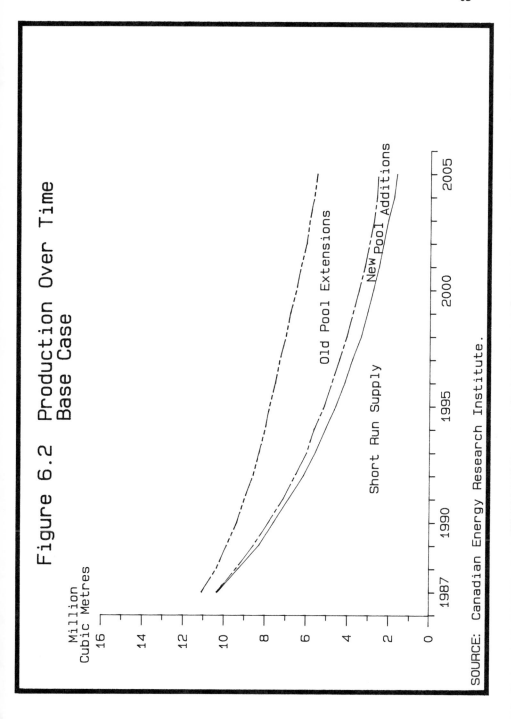

Figure 6.2   Production Over Time
Base Case

Million
Cubic Metres

Old Pool Extensions

New Pool Additions

Short Run Supply

SOURCE: Canadian Energy Research Institute.

EOR in this study, our percentages are lower for extensions and higher for discoveries than they would be with EOR included. The comparable percentage adjusted for the inclusion of EOR would be 21.05 which is approximately equal to our base case estimate.

Comparing Fisher's percentages to those predicted by our model is only reasonable if the maturity of oil and gas development in the Province of Saskatchewan can be compared in general terms with the maturity of the entire United States. One may have some difficulty deciding which area is more or less mature. It is simply interesting to observe that Fisher's estimates are very close to the estimates produced by CERI's model.

6.4 Finding Costs

In future analysis, this modelling system can be used to estimate future finding costs of oil in Saskatchewan. These finding costs will be the exploration costs of discovering a new pool divided by the sizes of the new pools discovered. This calculation is expected to decline over time as a result of the decline in the size of the pools, but will provide an interesting comparison of the relative economics of each play.

6.5 Conclusion

Supply of oil in Saskatchewan is clearly responsive to large changes in oil prices and economic conditions. A drop in prices to a competitive floor for one year will affect supply marginally. A price drop for several years is likely to have a very significant effect. Since this industry is complicated by the exhaustible nature of the resource and largely affected by profit expectations, supply response is very difficult to measure without the aid of complex models and computer processing.

The model created during this study has been based upon new geological information and the application of new statistical techniques to that information. Existing production statistics from the Saskatchewan Government data base were used. These two basic data sources give the model a solid footing. In any forecast, assumptions must be made and this report is no exception. However, if there is disagreement concerning the assumptions which have been made in this report, new assumptions can easily be incorporated and tested within the modelling system. Such exercises are encouraged and available by contacting the Canadian Energy Research Institute.

Footnotes

[1]William L. Fisher, "Statement on Geoscience Research for the Sustained Stable Production of Oil and Gas in the U.S." This paper was a submission to the U.S. House of Representatives, Subcommittee on Energy Research and Development and the Committee on Science, Space and Technology, July 16, 1987.

Chapter 7

IMPLICATIONS OF SASKATCHEWAN
OIL SUPPLY ANALYSIS

7.1 Security of Supply

Given the results of this analysis, the security of Saskatchewan's supply of conventional oil can be viewed from two perspectives.
The first perspective tells us that if oil prices drop below a competitive floor of $10 per barrel, Saskatchewan short-run production will
fall. However, because of the relatively low elasticities of the
short-run supply, relaxation of royalty levels could maintain the bulk
of such production, depending upon the severity of the price collapse.
Referring to the short-run supply curve in Figure 2.2, supply does not
rapidly fall until the price drops to below $10 per barrel Cdn. This
result seems to be consistent with the experience of Saskatchewan
during the price collapse of 1986. It contributes significantly to
Saskatchewan's security of supply to know that oil production will
continue to be substantial even at relatively low world oil prices.

The second perspective is that the long-run supply can change
dramatically, given different price levels. This means that if world
demand increases and prices rise, additional reserves and production
are available from Saskatchewan. Such a result also suggests that
price support programs, if considered in the future, may be successful
in promoting continued production from reserves in Saskatchewan.

7.2 Uncertainty and its Effects

In our analysis we have attempted to measure the effects of
price changes on the supply of oil in Saskatchewan, assuming that the
price and economic changes are known. This means that the entrepreneurs and producers will invest and produce up to the point where the
marginal cost of production to industry is equal to the marginal
benefits, given certain prices offered for their oil. If we introduce
uncertainty regarding future prices into the analysis, entrepreneurs
may be a little more wary of such investments. During most of
the historical period over which the activity estimates were

made, oil prices were stable and then climbed consistently over time. Recently, prices have fallen rapidly and then recovered, but continue to remain weak. One effect of such uncertainty regarding the future path of crude oil prices is that investors demand a higher return on investment before a given activity will be undertaken.[1] In order to take account of the effects of price volatility, we could raise the rate of return required before new investment takes place and observe the effect upon the supply curve. The uncertainty of future prices can affect both short-run maintenance and long-run exploration and development investments. When observing the effects of price instability on short-run production we find the effect is minimal. This minimal effect results from the relatively low levels of investment and the relative security of the results of such investments on short-run supply. The exploration and development investments of the long-run supply curve do exhibit a significant response to future oil price uncertainty.

7.3 Uncertainty and Expectations

As the world oil market matures, additional price expectations will develop. Those expectations will develop as the new market environment becomes better known around the world. Our modelling system and our historical econometric analysis embodies the expectations of the 1970s and early 1980s. Expectations in the 1990s may be different than those of these earlier periods; as new expectations develop, the activity model can be adapted to account for those changes.

7.4 Recovery and Existing Reserves

An emerging issue in the supply of oil and gas is the ultimate recovery of existing reserves. Recent papers by William L. Fisher[2] have brought out the point that, in the U.S., most of the reserve additions of oil in the past decade have come from reserves growth rather than from new fields. He suggests that the percentage recovery of newly discovered reserves could be increased by reasonable additional research and fairly inexpensive infill drilling. Although this issue is relatively new, the idea is creating much interest in the policy community. Original runs of this modelling system for the Province of Saskatchewan indicate that large initial production rates on infill and extension wells, which would coincide with Fisher's hypothesis of higher than expected recovery factors for existing reserves due to further drilling, will generate substantial additional reserves in the province.

This is an important issue for the Province of Saskatchewan. Fisher's work has been concentrated on the characteristics of oil recovery in Texas. He points out that infill drilling based upon simple acreage spacing may not be the most efficient practice. He suggests that the available geological information may not be optimally used when planning the development of a reservoir. Therefore, more careful infill drilling may permit large increases in recoverable reserves from existing reservoirs.

The recent intensity of infill drilling in Saskatchewan has been reflected in increased productivity. The limits to the amount of infill and extension drilling which may take place economically are under debate. Fisher's approach raises some interesting questions about the assumed upper limits of future reserves growth.

Further study undertaken in 1982 and 1983 resulted in estimates of additional recovery from the major oil plays in Texas. A target of an additional 20 percent of the oil in place was established by this study. This oil was expected to be recoverable through "nontertiary techniques." This would raise recovery from an extimated 38 percent to 58 percent of oil in place. The resulting increase in oil supply from such an increase in estimated recovery is substantial. From an economic perspective, because this recovery is based upon infill drilling rather than EOR techniques, the potential is even more significant.

The potential for additional recovery from known reservoirs seems to overshadow reserves from new discoveries. Therefore, in order to further refine estimates of future supplies of oil in Saskatchewan, an important area of focus is infill drilling in existing fields.

Footnotes

[1]Robert S. Pindyck, "The Optimal Production of an Exhaustible Resource when Price is Exogenous and Stochastic," Scandinavian Journal of Economics, 1981.

[2]W. L. Fisher and W. E. Galloway, "Potential for Additional Oil Recovery in Texas." Bureau of Economic Geology, University of Texas at Austin, Austin, Texas, 1983.

[3]Noel Tyler, W. E. Galloway, C. M. Garretty Jr., and T. E. Ewing, "Oil Accumulation, Production Characteristics, and Targets for Additional Recovery in Major Oil Reservoirs of Texas," Bureau of Economic Geology, The University of Texas at Austin, Austin, Texas, 1984.

Chapter 8

USES OF THE MODELLING SYSTEM

8.1 Model Uses

One of the objectives of building this model was to test the supply response to large changes in the price of oil. The results of this study show a wide range of supplies which would be available at different prices. This model easily allows the analyst to change royalty structures, operating cost levels, and other economic parameters. Other assumptions, such as decline rates, initial production rates or recovery percentages can also be changed, but involve program changes.

Since the model is essentially a disaggregated model, these changes can be made on a region-by-region or even play-by-play basis. Different assumptions are likely to have different effects on different regions. The supply response can be analyzed both in terms of production capacity and reserves available to be produced. This allows more flexibility in the model. Price forecasts which rise and fall over the forecast period can be used to test how wells may be shut in and reactivated in the future (although this feature requires additional processing).

8.2 Enhanced Oil Recovery (EOR)

This model has been built in such a way as to allow the integration of an EOR analysis. In order to accomplish this new section, a screening process for existing and newly discovered reservoirs is needed and a forecast of EOR wells must be generated. Given these two additional inputs the model will run an EOR case dividing the supply results into short-run conventional, short-run EOR, long-run conventional and long-run EOR. The extension of the current modelling framework to the analysis of EOR will form the basis of a future Canadian Energy Research Institute (CERI) study.

8.3 Other Projects

The methodology used in constructing this system could be very useful for areas other than Saskatchewan. Presently the data and methodology are available to undertake this analysis for the Province of Alberta. This project would require the use of a larger computer because of the larger data base and processing requirements. However, much of the background and theoretical work from the Saskatchewan study can be applied directly to an analysis of crude oil supply in Alberta.

Other regions, such as Texas, also lend themselves to this type of analysis. For Texas, the major preliminary work would involve creating the "playbooks" or pool size curves for the various pools in the Texas region. Once this process was accomplished, the building of the model would be straightforward. The major data requirement for these calculations is the existing pool size information on each play, average play characteristics, and a general geological understanding of each play.

8.4 Natural Gas

The same methodology can be adapted to estimates of short- and long-run supply of natural gas. There are some important differences dictated by the nature of the cost of producing different types of natural gas. These differences would encourage a slightly different economic modelling structure, but the same basic methodology could be used.

8.5 How to Use the System

In Appendix B we include a manual for the software system. The system runs on software designed and written by the Canadian Energy Research Institute and copies of this software can be obtained from CERI. CERI has also made use of a software product called RAM. This product was used to generate the matrices used for the marginal production rates. Although it may be possible to generate matrices for this purpose using other methods, the RAM system is very useful for general analysis of reservoir economics.

APPENDIX A

PRICE ASSUMPTIONS

CREATED BY THE
CANADIAN ENERGY RESEARCH INSTITUTE

TABLE A.1

SASKATCHEWAN OIL SUPPLY CURVE LOW PRICE ASSUMPTIONS
CRUDE OIL PRICES
(nominal $Cdn./m³)

Year	Area 1	Area 2	Area 3	Area 4	Area 5	Area 6	Average
1987	105.15	105.97	120.26	128.56	144.55	139.83	123.97
1988	54.38	55.20	61.20	64.57	71.56	69.72	62.93
1989	55.67	55.96	62.39	67.77	74.61	72.58	65.45
1990	57.57	57.85	64.14	70.60	77.28	75.29	68.06
1991	56.63	59.67	65.73	73.88	80.33	78.39	70.79
1992	61.93	62.20	68.06	76.97	83.20	81.34	73.62
1993	64.59	64.85	70.53	80.29	86.33	84.54	76.56
1994	67.51	67.76	73.27	83.80	89.65	87.89	79.63
1995	70.59	70.83	76.17	87.40	93.11	91.40	82.81
1996	73.41	73.66	79.22	90.89	96.83	95.05	86.12
1997	76.35	76.61	82.39	94.53	100.70	98.86	89.57
1998	79.40	79.67	85.69	98.31	104.73	102.81	93.15
1999	82.58	82.86	89.11	102.24	108.92	106.92	96.88
2000	85.88	86.18	92.68	106.33	113.28	111.20	100.75
2001	89.31	89.62	96.38	110.59	117.81	115.65	104.78
2002	92.89	93.21	100.24	115.01	122.52	120.27	108.97
2003	96.60	96.94	104.25	119.61	127.42	125.09	113.33
2004	100.47	100.81	108.42	124.39	132.52	130.09	117.86
2005	104.49	104.85	112.76	129.37	137.82	135.29	122.58

SOURCE: Canadian Energy Research Institute.

TABLE A.2

SASKATCHEWAN OIL SUPPLY CURVE BASE CASE ASSUMPTIONS

Year	Crude Oil Prices (nominal Cdn. $/m^3$)						All Natural Gas Areas (nominal $/10^3 m^3$)
	Area 1	Area 2	Area 3	Area 4	Area 5	Area 6	
1987	105.27	106.09	120.39	128.71	144.71	139.99	59.27
1988	117.05	117.68	131.73	138.98	154.04	150.07	60.34
1989	120.52	121.15	135.07	146.73	161.53	157.12	65.31
1990	127.51	128.14	142.07	156.37	171.17	166.76	75.96
1991	129.02	135.95	149.75	168.34	183.01	178.61	95.83
1992	146.60	147.23	161.09	182.20	196.94	192.53	105.06
1993	157.06	157.69	171.49	195.24	209.92	205.57	114.65
1994	169.22	169.85	183.65	210.04	224.72	220.31	124.23
1995	182.26	182.89	196.69	225.67	240.41	236.00	133.81
1996-end	Escalate at 6% per annum						

SOURCE: Canadian Energy Research Institute.

TABLE A.3

SASKATCHEWAN OIL SUPPLY CURVE HIGH PRICE ASSUMPTIONS

CRUDE OIL PRICES

(nominal $Cdn./m^3)

Year	Area 1	Area 2	Area 3	Area 4	Area 5	Area 6	Average
1987	105.15	105.97	120.26	128.56	144.55	139.83	123.97
1988	163.15	165.61	183.61	193.70	214.69	209.16	188.79
1989	170.22	171.11	190.77	207.23	228.14	221.91	200.11
1990	179.41	180.30	199.89	220.01	240.84	234.64	212.12
1991	179.88	189.54	208.78	234.69	255.15	249.00	224.85
1992	200.51	201.37	220.33	249.20	269.36	263.33	238.34
1993	213.14	214.00	232.72	264.95	284.87	278.97	252.64
1994	227.05	227.90	246.41	281.83	301.53	295.61	267.80
1995	241.96	242.80	261.12	299.59	319.16	313.31	283.87
1996	256.48	257.37	276.78	317.57	338.31	332.10	300.90
1997	271.87	272.81	293.39	336.62	358.61	352.03	318.95
1998	288.18	289.18	310.99	356.82	380.13	373.15	338.09
1999	305.47	306.53	329.65	378.23	402.93	395.54	358.37
2000	323.80	324.92	349.43	400.92	427.11	419.27	379.88
2001	343.23	344.42	370.40	424.97	452.74	444.43	402.67
2002	363.82	365.08	392.62	450.47	479.90	471.10	426.83
2003	385.65	386.99	416.18	477.50	508.69	499.36	452.44
2004	408.79	410.21	441.15	506.15	539.22	529.32	479.59
2005	433.32	434.82	467.62	536.52	571.57	561.08	508.36

SOURCE: Canadian Energy Research Institute.

APPENDIX B

THE SASKATCHEWAN OIL SUPPLY MODEL

CREATED BY THE
CANADIAN ENERGY RESEARCH INSTITUTE

Appendix B

THE SASKATCHEWAN OIL SUPPLY MODEL

B.1 Description of the System

The system consists of five (5) programs, eight (8) data bases, and two (2) index files. These programs and data bases are written in D-Base III+ and are currently running on an IBM AT.

In order to use the system, once it has been installed, a simple command is typed and the system will then prompt you for further inputs. Most simple inputs can be accomplished with little difficulty; however, because the system is fairly complex, programming changes may be required for some types of analysis.

B.2 Program Description

SASK.PRG

This program is the main driver. It checks to make sure all files and program files are present. If files are missing, it will give a message stating which files are/are not there. If all files are present, it will then execute the other four programs; otherwise the run is aborted.

ACTIVITY.PRG

The activity program forecasts wells to be drilled in the future. It uses the activity data base file by using the activity index file. This program processes each record by using field variables to calculate other field variables stored in the current record of the activity data base (see Activity.DBF description for created fields).

DISCOV.PRG

The discover program randomly chooses pools to be discovered each year. This program uses three (3) data bases and creates a fourth. They are: ACTIVITY.DBF, ISPG.DBF, AV_FILE.DBF and PRM1.DBF, respectively. The program goes through the Activity data base one record at a time. It takes the number of SEWELLS and randomly selects an equal number of records from the ISPG file that are of the same year and area.

DEV.PRG

The development program designates development wells as either wells drilled in conjunction with newly discovered pools or wells drilled as extensions to other pools. The program sets production rates and classifications for these development wells. This program uses three (3) data bases and creates a fourth. These files are PRM1.DBF., ACTIVITY.DBF, MATRIX.DBF, and ADDITION.DBF, respectively. It goes through the PRM1 file one record at a time, checking the production level with the minimum production level of the MATRIX file. If the production rate of the PRM1 record is above minimum, it will then assign to this record other values such as Crown or freehold, a water production level and an average rate of oil production. These again depend on the area the well is in. Next, the well is added to the Additions data base. When the PRM1 file is finished the program executes the same operations on the Activity data base.

CLASS.PRG

This classification program uses three (3) data bases and creates a fourth. The data bases used are SASK.DBF, MATRIX.DBF, ADDITION.DBF and SUM.DBF, respectively. The program screens the Saskatchewan data base and, depending on area, year, and other values in the record, assigns values to the two variables, COD and WAT. COD stands for code and, depending on values in the record, can be assigned a value from 1 to 9 (explained under the matrix definition). WAT is the amount of water produced at the well. This variable is assinged a value of 1, 2, or 3 depending on the area and amount of water. Next, the oil production is declined depending on which year it started producing. This amount is checked for a shut-off rate in the MATRIX data base. If the production rate is above the matrix minimum level, the production amount is added to the appropriate total variable for area and code. When all qualifying records (year of well) are processed, the totals are written to the SUM data base for that year. The year is incremented and the process is repeated. Once all the SASK.DBF records have been processed, the Additions data base is put through the same process.

B.3 Data Base File Structure

SASK.DBF

SASK.DBF contains the well data base from the Government of Saskatchewan, which has been sorted and carved down to the essential data required for this analysis. This data base is the largest in the system and forms the basis of the short-run analysis.

ACTIVITY.DBF

This data base contains the input values for the activity model. This data base must be changed as price, cost, or royalty assumptions are changed. This data base also contains the output of the activity model once the system has been run. The description of the fields in this data base are presented below:

```
POIL          - OIL PRICE
PGAS          - GAS PRICE
ROYOIL        - OIL ROYALTIES
ROYGAS        - OPERATING COSTS
SUCCESS       ⌉
PROFIT        |
DUF           |
DUP           ├ DEFINED IN THE SASK. ACTIVITY MODEL DEFINITION
DRILLCOST     |
EWEIGHT       |
SWEIGHT       |
WPGAS         ⌋
WELLS         - NUMBER OF WELLS PER YEAR                    ⌉ CALCULATED
EWELLS        - NUMBER OF EXPLORATION WELLS PER YEAR        | IN THE
DWELLS        - NUMBER OF DEVELOPMENT WELLS PER YEAR        | ACTIVITY
SDWELLS       - NUMBER OF SUCCESSFUL DEVELOPMENT            | PROGRAM
                WELLS PER YEAR                              |
EORWELL       - NUMBER OF SUCCESSFUL EOR WELLS PER YEAR     ⌋
```

AV-FIL.DBF

This data base contains the average characteristics of pools in Saskatchewan. This information was calculated by taking existing pools in each play and averaging the values. The field definitions are presented below:

```
ES_RE_PR      - ESTIMATED RECOVERY PRIMARY
ES_RE_EN      - ESTIMATED RECOVERY ENHANCED
NET_PAY_M     - NET PAY IN METRES
AV_POROS      - AVERAGE POROSITY
```

```
WAT SA      - WATER SATURATION
FOR VO      - FORMATION VOLUME FACTOR
AV DEP M    - AVERAGE DEPTH IN METRES
IN RE PR    - INITIAL RECOVERY PRIMARY
IN RE EN    - INITIAL RECOVERY ENHANCED
PR WE SP    - PRIMARY WELL SPACING
DECLIN      - DECLINE RATE
P TIME      - PRIMARY RECOVERY, LIFE TIME
S TIME      - ENHANCED RECOVERY, LIFE TIME
E TIME      - TIME BETWEEN BEGINNING OF PRIMARY AND BEGINNING
              OF ENHANCED.
```

ISPG.DBF

This data base contains the undiscovered pools hypothesized to exist by the ISPG. The pools are listed in order of size and by play name.

MATRIX.DBF

This data base file holds the minimum production rates of all areas. Each area can be divided into nine (9) different types, as well as being further divided into three (3) different water production levels, for a total of 71 fields.

Mnemonic Scheme of Fields, in MATRIX.DBF

A123

All data base field names must start with a character.
"A" stands for area.
"1" The first number after the "A" stands for the actual area the well is in.
"2" The second number after the "A" stands for the type of well (the types 1-9 are explained below)

"3" The third number after the "A" stands for the water production level of the well, either a 1, 2, or 3.

Types of Well

1 - Exempt
2 - Crown Conventional
3 - Crown EOR
4 - Free Conventional
5 - Free EOR
6 - Old Crown
7 - New Crown
8 - Old Freehold
9 - New Freehold

PRM1.DBF

This data base contains the characteristics of wells located in newly discovered pools. This data base is created by the Discovery.PRG program.

S_P_WELL	– NUMBER OF SECONDARY PRODUCING WELLS
S_I_PR_RT	– SECONDARY INITIAL PRODUCTION RATE
I_P_RATE	– INITIAL PRODUCTION RATE
P_OIL	– OIL PRODUCTION
N_P_WELL	– NUMBER OF PRODUCING WELLS
P_WAT	– WATER PRODUCTION
DEEP	– DEPTH OF WELL
CR_OR_FR	– WELL IS EITHER CROWN OR FREEHOLD
AR_EXT	– AREAL EXTENT
AREA	– AREA WELL IS IN
YEAR	– YEAR STARTED PRODUCING
PL_LETT	– PLAY LETTER

ADDITION.DBF

This is created from the class program. The structure of this data base is identical to PRM1.DBF with the exception of one field noted below.

Type   – THE TYPE OF WELL (EXPLORATION OR DEVELOPMENT)

SUM.DBF

This data base holds the production for each of the areas and for well types 1 to 9 (described in the Matrix.DBF definition).

B.4 System Requirements

Computer: PC, XT or AT DOS-compatible computer, with minimum of six (6) megabytes of hard disk storage.

Software: DOS 2.0 or higher.
Dbase III+.
Using a clipper compiler is recommended because the run time under clipper is much shorter.

Installation: Dbase III+ should already be installed in the computer under a directory off of the root directory called "DBASE" (if not, refer to the

Dbase manual on installation). Clipper should also be added to the Dbase directory.

From the Dbase directory, create another directory called "SASK" (refer to DOS manual on creating a new directory). Once created, all programs, data base files and index files of the Saskatchewan Oil Supply Curve Model should be copied in this new directory "SASK."

APPENDIX C

PRODUCTION RESULTS DIVIDED BY ROYALTY CATEGORY

CREATED BY THE
CANADIAN ENERGY RESEARCH INSTITUTE

Appendix C

PRODUCTION RESULTS DIVIDED BY ROYALTY CATEGORY

This appendix is divided into three major sections--one section for each test case. Each section contains the results of the test case divided by area, royalty category, and year of production. All results are measured in cubic metres of oil.

Each section is also divided into subsections containing short-run supply, new pool additions and old pool extensions. The last column of each page contains area totals and at the end of each subsection the yearly totals of each category are presented in an extra column. Summary results are presented in charts in Chapters 2 (Short Run) and 4 (Long Run).

C.1
Low Case Tables

SHORT RUN AREA ONE

AREA ONE TOTALS

YEAR	CROWN EXEMPT	FREEHOLD EXEMPT	NEW CROWN	NEW FREEHOLD	CROWN EOR	FREEHOLD EOR	AREA ONE TOTAL
86	249710	81431	1751342	655661	4034	232376	2974555
87	15028	2748	1608977	543626	3528	204485	2378391
88	4486	0	1054272	286177	2853	178290	1526078
89	3992	0	865534	221444	2540	158678	1252188
90	3552	0	723229	181365	2260	141223	1051630
91	3162	0	671898	166026	2012	124489	967587
92	2814	0	592086	143494	1790	111360	851545
93	2505	0	486065	103654	1593	97432	697249
94	1819	0	398652	85498	1418	86715	574102
95	1984	0	329339	58604	1262	77176	468366
96	1108	0	266220	38196	1123	66562	373209
97	986	0	220861	29546	1000	57364	309758
98	878	0	174214	25280	890	48323	249585
99	781	0	135119	21410	792	41654	199755
100	695	0	171145	22972	705	39637	235155
101	619	0	141050	17498	627	33404	193198
102	551	0	113199	13088	558	29014	156409
103	490	0	88913	8268	497	25822	123990
104	436	0	86505	7633	442	22321	117337
105	388	0	66892	5069	394	19203	91946
*** Total ***	295984	84179	9945513	2640510	30318	1795530	14792034

SHORT RUN AREA TWO

AREA TWO TOTALS

YEAR	CROWN EXEMPT	FREEHOLD EXEMPT	NEW CROWN	NEW FREEHOLD	AREA TWO TOTAL
86	52909	26310	554693	170406	804318
87	7893	4073	526032	166611	704609
88	4140	838	430208	139126	574313
89	0	0	387275	123166	510441
90	0	0	360822	117277	478098
91	0	0	333081	108681	441762
92	0	0	296065	96478	392543
93	0	0	277030	90805	367835
94	0	0	243574	79618	323192
95	0	0	227203	70408	297610
96	0	0	200889	68796	269685
97	0	0	176720	60182	236902
98	0	0	156766	53330	210096
99	0	0	137580	47413	184993
100	0	0	119840	42801	162641
101	0	0	104311	38230	142541
102	0	0	92318	33469	125787
103	0	0	80031	29697	109727
104	0	0	69289	26190	95479
105	0	0	58315	22481	80796
*** Total ***	64942	31221	4832041	1585164	6513368

SHORT RUN AREA THREE

AREA THREE TOTALS

YEAR	CROWN EXEMPT	FREEHOLD EXEMPT	NEW CROWN	NEW FREEHOLD	AREA THREE TOTAL
86	85681	4051	1648356	128207	1866295
87	2794	3162	1539045	112295	1657297
88	1036	0	1318825	95386	1415248
89	0	0	1173174	83410	1256584
90	0	0	1040421	73905	1114326
91	0	0	919746	66101	985846
92	0	0	814586	58373	872959
93	0	0	718068	52104	770172
94	0	0	629635	43126	672760
95	0	0	554775	39719	594494
96	0	0	486392	35246	521638
97	0	0	474622	31722	506344
98	0	0	418101	26999	445101
99	0	0	367992	24299	392292
100	0	0	322852	21350	344202
101	0	0	297477	19012	316489
102	0	0	260319	17111	277430
103	0	0	227609	14827	242435
104	0	0	198975	12568	211543
105	0	0	183219	10943	194162
*** Total ***	89511	7213	13594190	966703	14657618

SHORT RUN AREA FOUR

AREA FOUR TOTALS

YEAR	CROWN EXEMPT	FREEHOLD EXEMPT	NEW CROWN	NEW FREEHOLD	OLD CROWN	OLD FREEHOLD	AREA FOUR TOTAL
86	284393	142154	1215118	525698	36006	37805	2241174
87	54005	13287	1299405	577040	33034	34023	2010794
88	9299	787	1090366	420049	18597	17743	1556842
89	6255	731	997894	376305	12548	15874	1409606
90	5324	0	935147	343574	10658	12889	1307592
91	4940	0	867292	331740	10806	14180	1228958
92	4584	0	785266	295814	10028	12686	1108378
93	3772	0	715367	272600	8518	10740	1010996
94	4305	0	646655	251695	8636	9559	920850
95	3664	0	621977	234898	7335	8455	876329
96	3400	0	564776	216051	6807	8232	799267
97	3155	0	527508	196953	6317	7640	741574
98	2596	0	475948	181284	5862	7090	672779
99	2717	0	443092	166424	5440	6579	624253
100	2522	0	399582	153383	5049	6105	566640
101	2075	0	372102	139680	4193	5400	523450
102	1925	0	337633	125970	3891	5011	474430
103	2015	0	314388	117463	3246	3738	440849
104	1658	0	282939	107507	3351	3468	398924
105	1539	0	263438	98909	2795	3219	369899
*** Total ***	404143	156960	13155894	5133036	203119	230435	19283586

SHORT RUN AREA FIVE

AREA FIVE TOTALS

YEAR	CROWN EXEMPT	FREEHOLD EXEMPT	NEW CROWN	NEW FREEHOLD	AREA FIVE TOTALS
86	287095	175930	558846	198043	1219914
87	56842	30810	685213	301162	1074027
88	0	0	642601	276180	918781
89	0	0	571681	246494	818175
90	0	0	521102	223481	744583
91	0	0	472119	203373	675492
92	0	0	417833	181461	599294
93	0	0	369008	160580	529587
94	0	0	325239	141829	467068
95	0	0	285582	123902	409484
96	0	0	248495	108483	356977
97	0	0	215471	94300	309770
98	0	0	185121	80684	265805
99	0	0	157061	69607	226668
100	0	0	131422	58816	190238
101	0	0	112107	49228	161334
102	0	0	93439	40311	133750
103	0	0	77321	33065	110386
104	0	0	63415	27105	90519
105	0	0	49582	20236	69818
*** Total ***	343937	206740	6182657	2638339	9371672

SHORT RUN AREA SIX

AREA SIX TOTALS

YEAR	CROWN EXEMPT	FREEHOLD EXEMPT	NEW CROWN	NEW FREEHOLD	OLD CROWN	OLD FREEHOLD	TOTAL FOR AREA SIX	TOTAL FOR ALL AREAS
86	315582	181792	1294241	871787	76370	162815	2902586	12008843
87	76803	41713	1348695	858474	67334	145786	2538805	10363923
88	24812	0	1139250	644157	46016	104576	1958812	7950074
89	16030	0	1021463	562158	39866	87531	1727049	6974042
90	14310	0	934029	505338	35285	74999	1563962	6260192
91	13144	0	844502	471587	33438	75313	1437984	5737630
92	11961	0	752580	413389	29632	62633	1270195	5094914
93	10784	0	666437	362242	25784	56517	1121764	4497603
94	9813	0	588665	323622	19755	49730	991584	3949556
95	8930	0	517525	298578	16747	46367	888148	3534432
96	8126	0	494834	260011	14766	40542	818279	3139055
97	7289	0	437612	232088	13030	36968	726988	2831336
98	6633	0	382170	211167	11857	32580	644407	2487774
99	6036	0	354306	187934	10052	29163	587490	2215451
100	5184	0	309102	164192	7483	24575	510534	2009411
101	4717	0	268867	145293	7586	22461	448923	1785936
102	4193	0	249508	127091	5759	19383	405934	1573741
103	3606	0	217207	118134	5639	17077	361663	1389050
104	3767	0	187319	100982	4133	15202	311403	1225205
105	3428	0	175615	90708	3979	13208	286938	1093560
*** Total ***	555150	223505	12183927	6948931	474511	1117425	21503449	86121728

NEW POOL ADDITIONS AREA ONE

AREA ONE TOTALS

YEAR	CROWN EXEMPT	FREEHOLD EXEMPT	NEW CROWN	NEW FREEHOLD	CROWN EOR	FREEHOLD EOR	AREA ONE TOTAL
1987	0	0	0	0	0	0	0
1988	0	0	0	0	0	0	0
1989	0	0	0	0	0	0	0
1990	0	0	0	0	0	0	0
1991	6429	2755	0	0	0	0	9184
1992	13069	6126	0	0	0	0	19195
1993	14614	6943	4365	2182	0	0	28105
1994	13887	6943	10352	4852	0	0	36035
1995	13887	6943	15033	7229	0	0	43092
1996	12968	6943	19200	8318	0	0	47429
1997	12151	6025	20525	8318	0	0	47119
1998	10314	5208	19898	8318	0	0	43737
1999	8679	4289	19251	11717	0	0	43936
2000	9517	5268	28353	12294	0	0	55432
2001	10263	4592	27439	10990	0	0	53284
2002	8624	3923	25419	11253	0	0	49219
2003	6489	3774	25653	9684	0	0	45601
2004	6340	2566	26965	11413	0	0	47284
2005	3774	2566	25460	9730	0	0	41530
*** Total ***	151007	74866	268015	116297	0	0	610184

NEW POOL ADDITIONS AREA TWO

AREA TWO TOTALS

YEAR	CROWN EXEMPT	FREEHOLD EXEMPT	NEW CROWN	NEW FREEHOLD	AREA TWO TOTAL
1987	0	0	0	0	0
1988	0	0	0	0	0
1989	0	0	0	0	0
1990	0	0	0	0	0
1991	4145	0	0	0	4145
1992	6569	1382	0	0	7950
1993	6465	2650	2329	0	11444
1994	6682	2650	5536	1164	16032
1995	7950	2650	7411	2233	20244
1996	6569	1268	10296	3215	21348
1997	2537	0	12945	4115	19597
1998	0	0	14212	3778	17990
1999	0	0	13047	3468	16515
2000	0	0	11977	3184	15161
2001	0	0	10995	2923	13918
2002	0	0	10093	2683	12776
2003	0	0	9266	2463	11729
2004	0	0	8506	2261	10767
2005	0	0	7808	2076	9884
*** Total ***	40917	10601	124421	33563	209501

NEW POOL ADDITIONS AREA THREE

AREA THREE TOTALS

YEAR	CROWN EXEMPT	FREEHOLD EXEMPT	NEW CROWN	NEW FREEHOLD	AREA THREE TOTAL
1987	24525	0	0	0	24525
1988	22073	0	0	0	22073
1989	9933	0	9933	0	19865
1990	0	0	17879	0	17879
1991	0	0	16091	0	16091
1992	0	0	14482	0	14482
1993	0	0	13034	0	13034
1994	0	0	11730	0	11730
1995	0	0	10557	0	10557
1996	0	0	9502	0	9502
1997	0	0	8551	0	8551
1998	0	0	7696	0	7696
1999	0	0	6927	0	6927
2000	0	0	6234	0	6234
2001	16748	0	5611	0	22359
2002	15073	0	5049	0	20123
2003	6783	0	11327	0	18110
2004	0	0	16299	0	16299
2005	0	0	14669	0	14669
*** Total ***	95134	0	185571	0	280706

NEW POOL ADDITIONS AREA FOUR

AREA FOUR TOTALS

YEAR	CROWN EXEMPT	FREEHOLD EXEMPT	NEW CROWN	NEW FREEHOLD	OLD CROWN	OLD FREEHOLD	AREA FOUR TOTAL
1987	1551	775	0	0	0	0	2326
1988	4631	5406	0	0	0	0	10037
1989	7541	4349	668	0	0	0	12559
1990	5586	3640	5276	2972	0	0	17473
1991	1815	2305	9600	4321	0	0	18040
1992	1433	1433	10593	5160	0	0	18620
1993	1330	1330	9830	4789	0	0	17279
1994	0	1949	9897	3949	0	0	15795
1995	4499	2607	9611	5270	0	0	21986
1996	5602	3032	9139	5079	0	0	22852
1997	7328	4638	12151	5329	0	0	29446
1998	8531	6284	13225	6985	0	0	35025
1999	11738	5464	15416	8583	0	0	41201
2000	7868	4223	18419	10218	0	0	40728
2001	4167	1989	21598	12098	0	0	39851
2002	5405	2018	21798	12436	0	0	41657
2003	10876	7732	20819	12131	0	0	51557
2004	14321	5985	22237	12447	0	0	54991
2005	12780	5397	27294	15218	0	0	60690
*** Total ***	117000	70558	237570	126984	0	0	552112

NEW POOL ADDITIONS AREA FIVE

AREA FIVE TOTALS

YEAR	CROWN EXEMPT	FREEHOLD EXEMPT	NEW CROWN	NEW FREEHOLD	AREA FIVE TOTALS
1987	7335	3294	0	0	10629
1988	7049	5565	1017	339	13969
1989	6031	4927	6021	1675	18654
1990	9530	4227	8190	4846	26854
1991	10240	5893	10507	5419	32059
1992	11654	4347	13326	7448	36775
1993	12714	6734	17030	9285	45763
1994	13555	6388	20505	9681	52129
1995	15851	7990	24415	11690	59946
1996	10820	3763	27957	14832	57373
1997	3612	2087	33052	15526	54277
1998	4892	3030	31830	15264	55015
1999	6680	3285	30095	14457	54517
2000	13742	7646	30142	14057	65588
2001	14512	8392	29810	14564	67278
2002	12410	4629	34143	17730	68912
2003	5966	2158	36023	18680	62827
2004	0	937	38042	18191	57170
2005	2772	2313	35287	16754	57126
*** Total ***	169425	89605	427391	210438	896859

NEW POOL ADDITIONS AREA SIX

AREA SIX TOTALS

YEAR	CROWN EXEMPT	FREEHOLD EXEMPT	NEW CROWN	NEW FREEHOLD	OLD CROWN	OLD FREEHOLD	TOTAL FOR AREA SIX	TOTAL FOR ALL AREAS
1987	35081	37490	0	0	0	0	72571	110051
1988	49734	43582	5401	5401	0	0	104117	150196
1989	29923	37585	29050	24136	0	0	120694	171772
1990	8009	15603	45657	40562	0	0	109831	172037
1991	8352	3987	48458	51110	0	0	111907	191427
1992	11243	7615	44097	46166	0	0	109121	206143
1993	6930	7615	43429	45313	0	0	103287	218911
1994	14911	18539	45827	44536	0	0	123812	255533
1995	21024	21024	41702	43829	0	0	127579	283405
1996	24764	18590	44123	52232	0	0	139710	298213
1997	15095	10744	51943	53705	0	0	131487	290477
1998	16509	8824	53442	58648	0	0	137423	296887
1999	48185	48074	55514	53370	0	0	205143	368238
2000	68601	69370	54222	55874	0	0	248067	431210
2001	60766	58945	79982	84006	0	0	283699	480388
2002	26371	26371	101710	103714	0	0	258166	450853
2003	2916	1242	116121	118377	0	0	238656	428480
2004	2260	2372	106064	107723	0	0	218419	404930
2005	2270	1130	97546	99057	0	0	200003	383903
*** Total ***	452942	438700	1064288	1087760	0	0	3043691	5593053

OLD POOL EXTENSIONS AREA ONE

AREA ONE TOTALS

YEAR	CROWN EXEMPT	FREEHOLD EXEMPT	NEW CROWN	NEW FREEHOLD	CROWN EOR	FREEHOLD EOR	AREA ONE TOTAL
1987	75320	38046	0	0	0	0	113366
1988	39214	20677	24085	9451	0	0	93427
1989	12570	6089	39758	18079	0	0	76497
1990	12639	6621	39403	17803	0	0	76466
1991	11118	6062	37763	15703	0	0	70545
1992	11595	5189	37431	16705	0	0	70921
1993	11773	5905	32335	12800	0	0	62814
1994	12349	5875	28847	10079	0	0	57150
1995	12775	6071	19354	5393	0	0	43593
1996	11393	6893	18277	6855	0	0	43419
1997	11178	5230	16572	7021	0	0	40001
1998	9121	4213	16382	6633	0	0	36348
1999	7071	4085	15886	9887	0	0	36929
2000	8374	3311	25885	11647	0	0	49217
2001	6237	2717	24213	8957	0	0	42125
2002	4721	1924	22958	9427	0	0	39031
2003	3622	2680	20296	7558	0	0	34157
2004	2241	2488	21244	7830	0	0	33803
2005	3293	768	18265	7575	0	0	29902
*** Total ***	266605	134844	458956	189404	0	0	1049810

OLD POOL EXTENSIONS AREA TWO

AREA TWO TOTALS

YEAR	CROWN EXEMPT	FREEHOLD EXEMPT	NEW CROWN	NEW FREEHOLD	AREA TWO TOTAL
1987	37635	11901	0	0	49536
1988	14821	6717	11519	2975	36032
1989	2299	1810	27456	7624	39189
1990	4947	1558	26689	8168	41361
1991	3427	461	26438	8945	39272
1992	2936	930	26660	8196	38722
1993	4717	2211	26285	6619	39833
1994	3312	1959	25595	7690	38556
1995	3953	1792	25784	7510	39040
1996	5747	1542	24619	8132	40040
1997	5128	1377	24638	7506	38649
1998	6162	2189	23838	7309	39499
1999	5413	1939	23372	7171	37895
2000	4919	1774	24008	7095	37797
2001	5690	1527	22712	7943	37871
2002	4658	452	21069	7997	34176
2003	4071	912	19522	7003	31507
2004	4623	2167	18440	6177	31408
2005	3527	1920	17134	6190	28771
*** Total ***	127985	45140	415779	130249	719153

OLD POOL EXTENSIONS AREA THREE

AREA THREE TOTALS

YEAR	CROWN EXEMPT	FREEHOLD EXEMPT	NEW CROWN	NEW FREEHOLD	AREA THREE TOTAL
1987	41944	4892	0	0	46836
1988	30111	4700	16171	1373	52355
1989	18813	1503	33975	3962	58254
1990	20410	1662	37489	4919	64480
1991	18535	3149	42758	4427	68870
1992	18965	1488	46898	5331	72682
1993	19595	1645	48442	6137	75819
1994	18792	3118	53349	5523	80782
1995	17483	3102	55110	6304	81999
1996	18955	1466	55087	6999	82508
1997	20507	1621	57505	7619	87252
1998	17641	3071	59114	6857	86684
1999	19667	1451	61665	7484	90268
2000	22038	1605	59865	8042	91549
2001	21283	3041	63803	7238	95365
2002	20953	3026	64620	7814	96411
2003	21494	3010	66655	8326	99486
2004	24339	2995	65983	8780	102097
2005	25911	2980	68855	9182	106929
*** Total ***	417436	49527	957345	116318	1540626

OLD POOL EXTENSIONS AREA FOUR

AREA FOUR TOTALS

YEAR	CROWN EXEMPT	FREEHOLD EXEMPT	NEW CROWN	NEW FREEHOLD	OLD CROWN	OLD FREEHOLD	AREA FOUR TOTAL
1987	171089	85214	0	0	0	0	256303
1988	105916	67019	70106	34673	0	0	277715
1989	70550	43337	147339	69990	0	0	331216
1990	67161	42750	175836	87576	0	0	373323
1991	74846	42871	201680	100519	0	0	419917
1992	72911	43642	225933	108398	0	0	450885
1993	76812	43526	248311	120967	0	0	489617
1994	74858	41829	262768	130440	0	0	509895
1995	78576	41331	286967	140762	0	0	547636
1996	77010	41416	303689	146101	0	0	568216
1997	78922	41006	318661	156420	0	0	595009
1998	75945	40929	328066	159480	0	0	604419
1999	81193	40584	341404	168945	0	0	632126
2000	78861	40042	349918	171165	0	0	639985
2001	79440	40273	361863	178861	0	0	660437
2002	78571	39240	365665	180934	0	0	664410
2003	77758	38397	375148	187593	0	0	678896
2004	75835	38473	377922	188493	0	0	680722
2005	75490	37318	386799	192325	0	0	691932
*** Total ***	1571744	849197	5128075	2523641	0	0	10072657

OLD POOL EXTENSIONS AREA FIVE

AREA FIVE TOTALS

YEAR	CROWN EXEMPT	FREEHOLD EXEMPT	NEW CROWN	NEW FREEHOLD	AREA FIVE TOTALS
1987	52440	29100	0	0	81540
1988	7380	18728	28533	14662	69303
1989	2824	12788	47186	23544	86343
1990	1847	12742	54851	27408	95848
1991	9789	13443	61033	29823	114089
1992	9692	12741	65282	32957	120671
1993	10767	12550	69929	35152	128399
1994	11347	13158	73628	36917	135050
1995	14933	13238	77663	38741	144574
1996	13116	12775	81173	40855	147919
1997	13890	12855	84107	42410	153262
1998	14840	12892	86007	43239	156978
1999	16950	13467	88368	44442	163228
2000	16803	13127	89864	45487	165281
2001	17601	11848	90847	46675	166971
2002	16802	12237	92269	46761	168068
2003	18622	12801	92368	46690	170482
2004	18103	11995	92118	46887	169102
2005	18687	11951	91640	46971	169249
*** Total ***	286434	264437	1366866	689621	2607358

OLD POOL EXTENSIONS AREA SIX

AREA SIX TOTALS

YEAR	CROWN EXEMPT	FREEHOLD EXEMPT	NEW CROWN	NEW FREEHOLD	OLD CROWN	OLD FREEHOLD	TOTAL FOR AREA SIX	TOTAL FOR ALL AREAS
1987	153750	139196	0	0	0	0	292946	840526
1988	112496	88537	65611	53447	0	0	320091	848923
1989	65586	52508	111434	101944	0	0	331471	922969
1990	59219	47349	132119	117577	0	0	356264	1008742
1991	58587	47365	143174	127901	0	0	377027	1089819
1992	57928	46614	151920	136575	0	0	393038	1146920
1993	56840	45483	157864	141710	0	0	401897	1198378
1994	55787	44265	150667	140204	0	0	390924	1212356
1995	54895	45630	177796	151703	0	0	430024	1286866
1996	53457	43228	168836	144726	0	0	410247	1292349
1997	53047	42527	169144	149661	0	0	414378	1328552
1998	52476	45092	180091	148335	0	0	425995	1349922
1999	51356	42572	177264	150917	0	0	422109	1382555
2000	50533	44254	183805	147863	0	0	426455	1410283
2001	50153	40346	173939	151418	0	0	415857	1418626
2002	48781	42354	180059	139059	0	0	410253	1412350
2003	47536	39257	170811	138805	0	0	396408	1410936
2004	47237	37250	159509	126192	0	0	370187	1387320
2005	45870	39781	170613	141925	0	0	398189	1424972
*** Total ***	1175534	973610	2824657	2409961	0	0	7383761	23373365

C.2
Base Case Tables

SHORT RUN AREA ONE

AREA ONE TOTALS

YEAR	CROWN EXEMPT	FREEHOLD EXEMPT	NEW CROWN	NEW FREEHOLD	CROWN EOR	FREEHOLD EOR	AREA ONE TOTAL
86	249710	81431	1751342	655661	4034	232376	2974555
87	15028	2748	1608977	543626	3206	204128	2377713
88	6501	0	1430352	477614	2853	181674	2098994
89	5533	0	1244734	403345	2540	161690	1817841
90	4925	0	1106856	358674	2260	143904	1616619
91	4153	0	955662	299280	2012	127683	1388789
92	3901	0	864521	275281	1790	113986	1259480
93	3472	0	744751	237990	1593	101138	1088945
94	2927	0	668347	208167	1418	90013	970872
95	2605	0	587369	181600	1262	80111	852948
96	2163	0	501036	151749	1123	71299	727370
97	2064	0	443254	133746	1000	63225	643289
98	1713	0	389245	110968	890	56270	559086
99	1525	0	332003	99267	792	49681	483267
100	1357	0	283054	80966	705	44216	410298
101	1208	0	257266	70776	627	39192	369069
102	878	0	217412	57224	558	34881	310953
103	781	0	193370	51034	497	31044	276726
104	695	0	158324	40696	442	27505	227663
105	619	0	142850	35635	394	24065	203563
*** Total ***	311758	84179	13880727	4473300	29997	1878081	20658042

SHORT RUN AREA TWO

AREA TWO TOTALS

YEAR	CROWN EXEMPT	FREEHOLD EXEMPT	NEW CROWN	NEW FREEHOLD	AREA TWO TOTAL
86	52909	26310	554693	170406	804318
87	8249	4073	524041	165145	701508
88	5858	1108	481529	153947	642443
89	0	0	442846	140395	583242
90	0	0	408792	129422	538214
91	0	0	376758	119046	495804
92	0	0	345042	109067	454109
93	0	0	316824	100123	416947
94	0	0	290002	91913	381915
95	0	0	266075	84376	350452
96	0	0	242306	77135	319441
97	0	0	222972	70810	293782
98	0	0	203559	64855	268414
99	0	0	187197	59673	246870
100	0	0	171977	54525	226502
101	0	0	155606	50054	205660
102	0	0	141026	45606	186632
103	0	0	131133	41974	173106
104	0	0	118846	38022	156868
105	0	0	109506	34981	144487
*** Total ***	67016	31491	5690730	1801477	7590715

SHORT RUN AREA THREE

AREA THREE TOTALS

YEAR	CROWN EXEMPT	FREEHOLD EXEMPT	NEW CROWN	NEW FREEHOLD	AREA THREE TOTAL
86	85681	4051	1648356	128207	1866295
87	2794	3162	1537618	110737	1654311
88	1036	0	1383671	101664	1486372
89	0	0	1241580	91298	1332878
90	0	0	1114345	81436	1195782
91	0	0	1004836	73469	1078304
92	0	0	902757	65964	968721
93	0	0	812107	59057	871164
94	0	0	729855	53430	783285
95	0	0	652970	47836	700806
96	0	0	588505	43052	631558
97	0	0	527049	38747	565796
98	0	0	474705	34872	509578
99	0	0	425091	31275	456366
100	0	0	379786	27937	407723
101	0	0	343214	25422	368636
102	0	0	307035	22165	329200
103	0	0	273694	19806	293500
104	0	0	248268	17825	266093
105	0	0	221324	16043	237367
*** Total ***	89511	7213	14816766	1090242	16003733

SHORT RUN AREA FOUR

AREA FOUR TOTALS

YEAR	CROWN EXEMPT	FREEHOLD EXEMPT	NEW CROWN	NEW FREEHOLD	OLD CROWN	OLD FREEHOLD	AREA FOUR TOTAL
86	284393	142154	1215118	525698	36006	37805	2241174
87	55066	13287	1298453	567179	33034	33745	2000765
88	15211	1381	1237898	535299	30655	31316	1851759
89	10390	731	1151264	495736	28448	29061	1715630
90	8886	0	1069129	460776	26400	26969	1592160
91	6354	0	994671	427600	24499	25027	1478151
92	5897	0	923382	397006	22735	23225	1372245
93	5472	0	856519	368422	21098	21553	1273064
94	5078	0	794636	341895	19579	19831	1181020
95	4713	0	737947	317279	18169	18561	1096669
96	4373	0	680840	292547	16861	17078	1011700
97	4058	0	634306	272832	15647	15849	942692
98	3766	0	585296	251643	14521	14708	869934
99	3495	0	544631	234040	13475	13649	809290
100	3243	0	502632	216232	12505	12666	747278
101	3010	0	468400	201236	11605	11754	696005
102	2793	0	431585	185128	10769	10908	641183
103	2592	0	397086	173096	9994	10122	592890
104	2405	0	372295	158299	9153	9394	551546
105	2232	0	342580	148536	8606	8584	510539
*** Total ***	433430	157553	15238667	6570480	383761	391804	23175695

SHORT RUN AREA FIVE

AREA FIVE TOTALS

YEAR	CROWN EXEMPT	FREEHOLD EXEMPT	NEW CROWN	NEW FREEHOLD	AREA FIVE TOTALS
86	287095	175930	558846	198043	1219914
87	69033	30810	684828	299327	1083998
88	1070	0	680519	297361	978949
89	0	0	614324	267423	881747
90	0	0	557779	243376	801155
91	0	0	505348	220847	726195
92	0	0	455524	198245	653769
93	0	0	414031	176289	590320
94	0	0	373191	156867	530058
95	0	0	334359	146100	480459
96	0	0	300795	129914	430709
97	0	0	269893	115552	385445
98	0	0	240650	102642	343292
99	0	0	224264	95346	319610
100	0	0	201529	84512	286041
101	0	0	180227	75468	255695
102	0	0	160095	67134	227229
103	0	0	148341	62390	210730
104	0	0	131905	55682	187586
105	0	0	117290	49432	166723
*** Total ***	357198	206740	7153736	3041952	10759625

SHORT RUN AREA SIX

AREA SIX TOTALS

YEAR	CROWN EXEMPT	FREEHOLD EXEMPT	NEW CROWN	NEW FREEHOLD	OLD CROWN	OLD FREEHOLD	TOTAL FOR AREA SIX	TOTAL FOR ALL AREAS
86	315582	181792	1294241	871787	76370	162815	2902586	12008843
87	74972	41713	1347622	839229	67726	142799	2514061	10332356
88	24307	0	1263044	791355	61274	129027	2269007	9327524
89	15726	0	1149409	704370	55759	115418	2040681	8372019
90	14310	0	1048245	643750	50741	106203	1863249	7607178
91	13022	0	952630	583191	46443	96965	1692252	6859495
92	11850	0	865272	530185	42018	87946	1537272	6245596
93	10784	0	785757	477410	37926	79871	1391748	5632188
94	9813	0	712346	435820	34386	72683	1265048	5112199
95	8930	0	646796	394900	31291	65856	1147773	4629108
96	8010	0	583189	353286	28475	58992	1031952	4152730
97	7395	0	531543	322824	25912	53674	941348	3772351
98	6633	0	479005	288780	23281	48475	846174	3396478
99	6036	0	437680	258679	21186	43709	767290	3082695
100	5493	0	394049	234426	19020	39435	692423	2770265
101	4999	0	353665	211496	17220	35723	623104	2518168
102	4466	0	316873	192109	15750	32508	561707	2256905
103	4139	0	293910	173696	14136	28812	514693	2061647
104	3555	0	263186	154463	12570	25897	459671	1849427
105	3301	0	240140	139876	11305	23425	418046	1680725
*** Total ***	553326	223505	13958600	8601633	692791	1450232	25480087	103667895

NEW POOL ADDITIONS AREA ONE

AREA ONE TOTALS

YEAR	CROWN EXEMPT	FREEHOLD EXEMPT	NEW CROWN	NEW FREEHOLD	CROWN EOR	FREEHOLD EOR	AREA ONE TOTAL
1987	11626	5813	0	0	0	0	17440
1988	22032	10541	0	0	0	0	32573
1989	22730	9640	8058	4605	0	0	45034
1990	19128	8499	17451	7951	0	0	53029
1991	16322	7703	24388	11283	0	0	59696
1992	24102	10850	27680	13030	0	0	75662
1993	25903	12672	32246	14612	0	0	85433
1994	28068	12836	39759	18915	0	0	99579
1995	27956	16383	45142	21612	0	0	111093
1996	24555	13088	52485	24754	0	0	114881
1997	26709	13090	57901	28612	0	0	126312
1998	29035	12795	61023	29975	0	0	132828
1999	26423	11305	65655	33032	0	0	136416
2000	14644	8107	70086	33581	0	0	126418
2001	3434	2561	72603	34856	0	0	113454
2002	7399	3575	66866	33021	0	0	110861
2003	10338	5914	60229	29638	0	0	106119
2004	11123	4144	57272	28751	0	0	101290
2005	5307	1327	55565	27950	0	0	90148
*** Total ***	356834	170846	814408	396177	0	0	1738265

NEW POOL ADDITIONS AREA TWO

AREA TWO TOTALS

YEAR	CROWN EXEMPT	FREEHOLD EXEMPT	NEW CROWN	NEW FREEHOLD	AREA TWO TOTAL
1987	5239	1048	0	0	6287
1988	7953	2010	0	0	9963
1989	6912	2010	3532	883	13337
1990	2886	962	6702	1694	12244
1991	4024	1006	8802	2438	16270
1992	6713	1930	8080	2238	18960
1993	6637	1930	9961	2902	21430
1994	11195	3732	12466	3512	30905
1995	13349	5386	13988	4072	36794
1996	12175	5165	19940	4921	42201
1997	13313	4036	23037	7970	48357
1998	11801	5270	27064	8500	52634
1999	22026	7943	30633	8961	69563
2000	24257	6803	32752	11604	75416
2001	16398	5542	43160	14245	79344
2002	16715	5534	48043	15512	85803
2003	16460	5526	50191	16675	88851
2004	26439	9805	53359	17735	107338
2005	28495	9425	56168	18709	112798
*** Total ***	252987	85060	447878	142571	928496

NEW POOL ADDITIONS AREA THREE

AREA THREE TOTALS

YEAR	CROWN EXEMPT	FREEHOLD EXEMPT	NEW CROWN	NEW FREEHOLD	AREA THREE TOTAL
1987	0	0	0	0	0
1988	0	0	0	0	0
1989	24525	0	0	0	24525
1990	22073	0	0	0	22073
1991	9933	0	9933	0	19865
1992	0	0	17879	0	17879
1993	2493	0	16091	0	18584
1994	2244	0	14482	0	16725
1995	1010	0	14043	0	15053
1996	1407	0	13548	0	14955
1997	1266	0	12193	0	13459
1998	1140	0	10974	0	12113
1999	4304	0	10902	0	15206
2000	3874	0	9812	0	13686
2001	11338	0	8831	0	20169
2002	7067	0	11085	0	18152
2003	6360	0	9977	0	16337
2004	2220	1110	14703	0	18033
2005	4218	999	13233	0	18449
*** Total ***	105470	2109	187684	0	295263

NEW POOL ADDITIONS AREA FOUR

AREA FOUR TOTALS

YEAR	CROWN EXEMPT	FREEHOLD EXEMPT	NEW CROWN	NEW FREEHOLD	OLD CROWN	OLD FREEHOLD	AREA FOUR TOTAL
1987	7906	5458	0	0	0	0	13363
1988	13828	10054	2272	1136	0	0	27290
1989	17304	11241	6808	2190	0	0	37543
1990	28408	4644	8590	9637	0	0	51279
1991	24066	8723	20765	10255	0	0	63809
1992	17567	11575	30298	12298	0	0	71738
1993	16036	7510	36553	16343	0	0	76443
1994	14515	6795	41220	18786	0	0	81316
1995	12870	10171	45075	19293	0	0	87409
1996	15028	7046	46497	22030	0	0	90601
1997	20735	5070	49901	24285	0	0	99990
1998	18361	11534	51491	25040	0	0	106425
1999	30724	12329	55544	25280	0	0	123877
2000	36852	13121	60155	30121	0	0	140250
2001	31128	15695	71133	32388	0	0	150344
2002	22791	14990	80893	37113	0	0	155786
2003	29906	12639	87024	41408	0	0	170977
2004	35982	13806	89290	43186	0	0	182264
2005	27599	16299	96401	46544	0	0	186843
*** Total ***	421605	198699	879911	417331	0	0	1917546

NEW POOL ADDITIONS AREA FIVE

AREA FIVE TOTALS

YEAR	CROWN EXEMPT	FREEHOLD EXEMPT	NEW CROWN	NEW FREEHOLD	AREA FIVE TOTALS
1987	12040	4441	0	0	16481
1988	20805	8208	3889	2593	35494
1989	22024	11290	9883	3645	46842
1990	19658	9050	18784	8866	56358
1991	13275	7437	26190	11631	58533
1992	13757	6830	31555	14706	66848
1993	25742	11818	32394	14802	84757
1994	27829	13354	35870	17678	94729
1995	20563	12288	46315	21851	101017
1996	18066	9646	52070	25471	105254
1997	25227	11960	54896	27063	119146
1998	27762	13245	56439	28826	126271
1999	20516	11639	64335	32031	128521
2000	17165	9144	68731	34533	129574
2001	20624	12963	69649	35191	138427
2002	31335	15694	70507	34684	152220
2003	32481	15781	74099	38176	160537
2004	26694	13780	82085	41352	163911
2005	21438	10921	87485	43739	163583
*** Total ***	417002	209489	885177	436838	1948506

NEW POOL ADDITIONS AREA SIX

AREA SIX TOTALS

YEAR	CROWN EXEMPT	FREEHOLD EXEMPT	NEW CROWN	NEW FREEHOLD	OLD CROWN	OLD FREEHOLD	TOTAL FOR AREA SIX	TOTAL FOR ALL AREAS
1987	13664	6636	0	0	0	0	20300	73871
1988	12434	9464	0	3603	0	0	25501	130820
1989	21583	31429	9098	5495	0	0	67605	234886
1990	35061	31874	10297	10820	0	0	88052	283035
1991	28564	36225	25407	23667	0	0	113863	332037
1992	29568	25668	36940	35355	0	0	127532	378619
1993	25954	16808	41090	49597	0	0	133449	420095
1994	53428	51987	49675	50534	0	0	205624	528879
1995	68178	68178	55519	54989	0	0	246864	598230
1996	59628	69506	85380	79006	0	0	293520	661412
1997	38554	48398	102433	100822	0	0	290207	697472
1998	19453	25106	120081	119682	0	0	284322	714594
1999	25963	16837	116752	119393	0	0	278944	752528
2000	19265	12589	115548	118072	0	0	265475	750818
2001	11167	13292	114477	112812	0	0	251748	753488
2002	5030	10593	111444	108200	0	0	235268	758090
2003	18757	20651	104046	102361	0	0	245817	788638
2004	26744	28490	96452	96798	0	0	248484	821319
2005	24043	19601	95520	101867	0	0	241031	812852
*** Total ***	537038	543332	1290161	1293074	0	0	3663605	10491682

OLD POOL EXTENSIONS AREA ONE

AREA ONE TOTALS

YEAR	CROWN EXEMPT	FREEHOLD EXEMPT	NEW CROWN	NEW FREEHOLD	CROWN EOR	FREEHOLD EOR	AREA ONE TOTAL
1987	75320	38676	0	0	0	0	113996
1988	77302	38820	29400	15066	0	0	160587
1989	72407	36447	59661	29679	0	0	198194
1990	70483	35226	84518	41831	0	0	232059
1991	68995	33505	103601	51235	0	0	257436
1992	68179	34589	122777	60550	0	0	286096
1993	68857	34981	136915	67202	0	0	307955
1994	69488	33721	150544	74940	0	0	328693
1995	68572	34071	162319	80737	0	0	345699
1996	63692	31937	172856	84771	0	0	353256
1997	55875	28120	182020	89944	0	0	355960
1998	46372	23145	186653	91484	0	0	347653
1999	37977	19097	187307	92952	0	0	337334
2000	32164	16032	182154	89091	0	0	319441
2001	26376	12713	177021	87147	0	0	303257
2002	21630	10622	168458	81753	0	0	282463
2003	17569	9125	159681	77753	0	0	264128
2004	14266	7909	147930	71047	0	0	241152
2005	12345	5990	138394	66937	0	0	223666
*** Total ***	967868	484828	2552208	1254120	0	0	5259024

OLD POOL EXTENSIONS AREA TWO

AREA TWO TOTALS

YEAR	CROWN EXEMPT	FREEHOLD EXEMPT	NEW CROWN	NEW FREEHOLD	AREA TWO TOTAL
1987	37686	11901	0	0	49587
1988	43463	12973	13009	4462	73907
1989	40381	13305	31759	10029	95474
1990	42382	13528	47590	14693	118193
1991	45602	13549	60794	19664	139610
1992	48388	15425	75822	23782	163418
1993	53594	16547	89662	27990	187793
1994	58445	17683	104675	33041	213844
1995	62532	19200	120725	37532	239990
1996	64158	19312	137465	42747	263682
1997	63012	19419	154435	47810	284677
1998	61922	19065	169913	52298	303198
1999	58578	18762	183248	56655	317244
2000	55334	17375	195373	59828	327910
2001	53192	16173	203793	63556	336714
2002	51465	15920	211277	65061	343723
2003	49264	15712	216568	66820	348364
2004	46097	14663	221419	68245	350424
2005	43548	13615	224023	69552	350738
*** Total ***	979045	304128	2461550	763767	4508490

OLD POOL EXTENSIONS AREA THREE

AREA THREE TOTALS

YEAR	CROWN EXEMPT	FREEHOLD EXEMPT	NEW CROWN	NEW FREEHOLD	AREA THREE TOTAL
1987	41944	4892	0	0	46836
1988	51635	6361	15171	1373	75541
1989	58224	6298	33975	3962	102459
1990	59306	7856	54923	6265	128350
1991	63572	7616	74681	8311	154179
1992	65948	6081	92525	11438	175993
1993	66272	7585	111985	12900	198743
1994	69424	8895	128364	14190	220872
1995	73399	8762	144388	16593	243142
1996	74985	8631	160208	18699	262522
1997	76714	8502	176407	20538	282161
1998	80141	8375	190506	22137	301160
1999	82493	9673	205028	23522	320717
2000	83354	10781	219224	24715	338075
2001	85897	10567	232892	26888	356245
2002	88822	10357	245089	28752	373020
2003	91245	10152	258220	30339	389955
2004	94121	9950	270468	31678	406217
2005	95202	11008	283066	32737	422073
*** Total ***	1402698	162341	2898121	335099	4798260

OLD POOL EXTENSIONS AREA FOUR

AREA FOUR TOTALS

YEAR	CROWN EXEMPT	FREEHOLD EXEMPT	NEW CROWN	NEW FREEHOLD	OLD CROWN	OLD FREEHOLD	AREA FOUR TOTAL
1987	140509	69881	0	0	0	0	210390
1988	153826	76467	57110	27677	0	0	315080
1989	152062	75677	121004	60181	0	0	408924
1990	147509	75238	181655	89687	0	0	494089
1991	146768	74161	235160	116998	0	0	573088
1992	147281	72164	283472	142030	0	0	644947
1993	145473	71994	328911	164624	0	0	711001
1994	143560	72906	370957	184461	0	0	771883
1995	141922	71021	408531	203771	0	0	825246
1996	136431	68022	443094	221640	0	0	869186
1997	130886	65944	474041	236647	0	0	907519
1998	126145	63279	499077	249452	0	0	937952
1999	120909	59913	520954	260587	0	0	962362
2000	115332	57516	538431	269319	0	0	980597
2001	109826	55292	552762	276009	0	0	993889
2002	105085	52127	563010	281464	0	0	1001687
2003	99872	49488	570610	285311	0	0	1005281
2004	94134	47351	575353	287284	0	0	1004122
2005	88489	44593	577408	288324	0	0	998814
*** Total ***	2446018	1223034	7301541	3645466	0	0	14616058

OLD POOL EXTENSIONS AREA FIVE

AREA FIVE TOTALS

YEAR	CROWN EXEMPT	FREEHOLD EXEMPT	NEW CROWN	NEW FREEHOLD	AREA FIVE TOTALS
1987	52285	26164	0	0	78449
1988	51183	26766	23248	11157	112353
1989	53127	26856	42564	21192	143738
1990	54045	26836	61095	30851	172827
1991	53200	26586	78546	39276	197608
1992	53302	26693	94101	47049	221145
1993	54770	26990	107558	53772	243090
1994	54174	27427	120994	60253	262848
1995	53689	27345	132811	66075	279920
1996	53002	26523	142777	71679	293981
1997	51715	25450	153086	76329	306581
1998	49770	24443	160702	80309	315224
1999	47187	23526	166939	83336	320987
2000	43848	22574	171957	85686	324065
2001	42036	21378	175910	87379	326703
2002	40720	20494	177286	88632	327132
2003	37980	19388	178370	89109	324848
2004	36594	17986	178704	89344	322628
2005	35183	17080	178066	88835	319164
*** Total ***	917810	460505	2344713	1170264	4893292

OLD POOL EXTENSIONS AREA SIX

AREA SIX TOTALS

YEAR	CROWN EXEMPT	FREEHOLD EXEMPT	NEW CROWN	NEW FREEHOLD	OLD CROWN	OLD FREEHOLD	TOTAL FOR AREA SIX	TOTAL FOR ALL AREAS
1987	96418	106995	0	0	0	0	203413	702671
1988	99378	110188	41121	45095	0	0	295781	1033250
1989	99118	109069	79844	88603	0	0	376634	1325423
1990	96218	106621	116347	128589	0	0	447775	1593294
1991	94122	104265	148198	163692	0	0	510277	1832198
1992	92012	101817	176025	194777	0	0	564632	2056230
1993	89252	99349	200665	221895	0	0	611162	2259743
1994	86448	96067	221962	245609	0	0	650087	2448228
1995	83455	93070	240081	266022	0	0	682628	2616625
1996	80877	89456	255395	282943	0	0	708671	2751298
1997	77168	84908	267920	297364	0	0	727360	2864257
1998	71995	80227	278467	308383	0	0	739073	2944260
1999	67627	75645	285768	316559	0	0	745600	3004244
2000	63760	70641	290218	321808	0	0	746427	3036515
2001	59697	66223	292646	324785	0	0	743351	3060159
2002	56303	62310	293129	324987	0	0	736729	3064755
2003	52635	57987	291775	323793	0	0	726190	3058766
2004	48486	53947	289365	320720	0	0	712519	3037063
2005	44836	50099	285206	315827	0	0	695969	3010424
*** Total ***	1459809	1618883	4054133	4491452	0	0	11624277	45699402

C.3
High Case Tables

SHORT RUN AREA ONE

AREA ONE TOTALS

YEAR	CROWN EXEMPT	FREEHOLD EXEMPT	NEW CROWN	NEW FREEHOLD	CROWN EOR	FREEHOLD EOR	AREA ONE TOTAL
86	249710	81431	1751342	655661	4034	232376	2974555
87	15028	2748	1608977	543626	3206	204128	2377713
88	7194	0	1498246	519529	3140	182361	2210470
89	6221	0	1311620	450793	2794	162301	1933730
90	5537	0	1166498	400790	2487	144448	1719760
91	4765	0	1018877	349418	2012	128074	1503145
92	4241	0	908298	311812	1790	113986	1340127
93	3774	0	804301	266950	1593	101448	1178067
94	3231	0	709154	237866	1418	90289	1041958
95	2875	0	627918	207287	1262	80357	919700
96	2447	0	544623	178655	1123	71518	798367
97	2178	0	485348	151860	1000	63456	703842
98	1837	0	418909	134880	890	56476	612991
99	1635	0	372282	112344	792	50264	537316
100	1455	0	319394	100834	705	44735	467123
101	1295	0	285198	83358	627	39814	410292
102	1075	0	240688	70237	558	35305	347864
103	957	0	212783	62909	497	31422	308567
104	852	0	186535	51400	442	27629	266858
105	758	0	162429	45892	394	24590	234062
*** Total ***	317065	84179	14633421	4936102	30764	1884976	21886507

SHORT RUN AREA TWO

AREA TWO TOTALS

YEAR	CROWN EXEMPT	FREEHOLD EXEMPT	NEW CROWN	NEW FREEHOLD	AREA TWO TOTAL
86	52909	26310	554693	170406	804318
87	8249	4073	524041	165145	701508
88	5858	1108	492116	158082	657164
89	0	0	455346	144496	599842
90	0	0	418837	133225	552062
91	0	0	384493	122301	506793
92	0	0	352123	111277	463401
93	0	0	323249	102466	425716
94	0	0	294966	93776	388742
95	0	0	271958	86086	358044
96	0	0	248121	78648	326770
97	0	0	228148	71812	299960
98	0	0	208671	66279	274949
99	0	0	190306	60395	250701
100	0	0	175852	55545	231397
101	0	0	160136	50599	210735
102	0	0	147534	46723	194257
103	0	0	133600	42556	176156
104	0	0	123523	38904	162427
105	0	0	112392	35863	148255
*** Total ***	67016	31491	5800104	1834585	7733196

AREA THREE TOTALS

YEAR	CROWN EXEMPT	FREEHOLD EXEMPT	NEW CROWN	NEW FREEHOLD	AREA THREE TOTAL
86	85681	4051	1648356	128207	1866295
87	2794	3162	1537618	110737	1654311
88	1036	0	1393926	105102	1500064
89	0	0	1253263	94453	1347716
90	0	0	1128155	85008	1213162
91	0	0	1013284	76370	1089654
92	0	0	909490	68541	978031
93	0	0	815481	61576	877057
94	0	0	736774	55314	792088
95	0	0	660627	49517	710144
96	0	0	593844	44042	637886
97	0	0	533069	38951	572020
98	0	0	478070	34872	512942
99	0	0	427316	31385	458701
100	0	0	383145	28247	411392
101	0	0	342525	24725	367250
102	0	0	305964	22007	327971
103	0	0	272851	19550	292401
104	0	0	242642	17420	260062
105	0	0	215308	15216	230525
*** Total ***	89511	7213	14891707	1111239	16099671

SHORT RUN AREA FOUR

AREA FOUR TOTALS

YEAR	CROWN EXEMPT	FREEHOLD EXEMPT	NEW CROWN	NEW FREEHOLD	OLD CROWN	OLD FREEHOLD	AREA FOUR TOTAL
86	284393	142154	1215118	525698	36006	37805	2241174
87	55066	13287	1298453	567179	33034	33745	2000765
88	15748	1381	1257425	554686	30655	32269	1892163
89	10553	731	1170952	515299	28448	29945	1755928
90	9038	0	1096723	478401	26400	27789	1628351
91	6495	0	1010749	443780	24499	25788	1511311
92	6027	0	936539	410286	22735	23932	1399519
93	5593	0	866703	380462	21098	22209	1296064
94	5190	0	806745	352761	19579	20609	1204886
95	4817	0	747134	328066	18169	19126	1117312
96	4373	0	694573	302620	16861	17749	1036176
97	4148	0	642576	280257	15647	16471	959099
98	3766	0	597589	260751	14521	15285	891912
99	3572	0	552647	241054	13475	14071	824820
100	3243	0	510630	223893	12505	13029	763301
101	3010	0	476641	207338	11605	12215	710809
102	2793	0	440320	192270	10769	11130	657282
103	2592	0	409742	177714	9994	10329	610371
104	2405	0	378642	164839	9274	9585	564745
105	2232	0	349837	152364	8606	8792	521831
*** Total ***	435057	157553	15449736	6759718	383882	401873	23587819

AREA FIVE TOTALS

YEAR	CROWN EXEMPT	FREEHOLD EXEMPT	NEW CROWN	NEW FREEHOLD	AREA FIVE TOTALS
86	287095	175930	558846	198043	1219914
87	69033	30810	684828	299327	1083998
88	1070	67	686236	302081	989453
89	0	0	621058	272448	893506
90	0	0	562678	246069	808748
91	0	0	509787	223501	733288
92	0	0	460555	201938	662493
93	0	0	416227	181840	598068
94	0	0	375202	163844	539046
95	0	0	341967	149872	491838
96	0	0	308483	134884	443367
97	0	0	278069	121193	399261
98	0	0	249607	108036	357643
99	0	0	229297	95969	325266
100	0	0	206690	85007	291696
101	0	0	185578	80802	266380
102	0	0	166824	71489	238313
103	0	0	149873	63958	213830
104	0	0	134031	56667	190697
105	0	0	119059	52710	171769
*** Total ***	357198	206807	7244894	3109677	10918575

SHORT RUN AREA SIX

AREA SIX TOTALS

YEAR	CROWN EXEMPT	FREEHOLD EXEMPT	NEW CROWN	NEW FREEHOLD	OLD CROWN	OLD FREEHOLD	TOTAL FOR AREA SIX	TOTAL FOR ALL AREAS
86	315582	181792	1294241	871787	76370	162815	2902586	12008843
87	74972	41716	1347622	839229	67726	142799	2514064	10332359
88	24642	0	1285282	833435	62512	134118	2339990	9589305
89	16030	0	1175122	755471	56886	122048	2125558	8656279
90	14444	0	1068132	685427	51766	110920	1930689	7852773
91	13144	0	970745	621667	46916	100713	1753185	7097377
92	11850	0	879700	559032	42503	90937	1584022	6427592
93	10784	0	800946	509967	38678	83082	1443457	5818428
94	9813	0	725937	457961	35197	74972	1303879	5270598
95	8930	0	660963	416706	32029	68224	1186852	4783890
96	8126	0	597898	377534	29146	61418	1074123	4316688
97	7395	0	545401	338247	26523	55732	973299	3907481
98	6729	0	492940	305186	24136	50413	879404	3529843
99	6124	0	449084	275931	21713	45684	798536	3195341
100	5573	0	406048	249379	19714	41411	722125	2887034
101	5071	0	369956	226210	17850	37635	656723	2622189
102	4615	0	333415	204332	16170	34109	592639	2358325
103	4199	0	304681	184878	14715	31039	539512	2140836
104	3767	0	274347	165894	13390	27910	485309	1930099
105	3428	0	246975	151518	12185	25050	439155	1745597
*** Total ***	555220	223508	14229434	9029792	706126	1501027	26245107	106470875

NEW POOL ADDITIONS AREA ONE

AREA ONE TOTALS

YEAR	CROWN EXEMPT	FREEHOLD EXEMPT	NEW CROWN	NEW FREEHOLD	CROWN EOR	FREEHOLD EOR	AREA ONE TOTAL
1987	10139	3802	0	0	0	0	13942
1988	36834	18557	0	0	0	0	55391
1989	58358	30774	7027	3012	0	0	99172
1990	65077	32578	28443	14599	0	0	140602
1991	51912	24956	51792	25631	0	0	154291
1992	41815	19001	72717	37447	0	0	170982
1993	36101	18134	81269	40070	0	0	175573
1994	26921	13146	89361	44713	0	0	174141
1995	20797	12415	92969	45185	0	0	171367
1996	19349	9395	91865	45830	0	0	166440
1997	25212	14025	90114	44400	0	0	173751
1998	32165	15263	87258	43744	0	0	178429
1999	26846	13986	91350	44925	0	0	177107
2000	23922	13334	93589	46588	0	0	177433
2001	19469	10206	93623	46528	0	0	169826
2002	24681	10909	91732	47330	0	0	174653
2003	21490	9999	89581	44819	0	0	165889
2004	13794	7134	90744	46131	0	0	157803
2005	8278	4726	87725	43421	0	0	144151
*** Total ***	563163	282341	1331165	664473	0	0	2841142

NEW POOL ADDITIONS AREA TWO

AREA TWO TOTALS

YEAR	CROWN EXEMPT	FREEHOLD EXEMPT	NEW CROWN	NEW FREEHOLD	AREA TWO TOTAL
1987	0	0	0	0	0
1988	0	0	0	0	0
1989	25609	8305	0	0	33914
1990	47733	15930	0	0	63663
1991	52343	17540	20998	6999	97880
1992	31706	10254	40226	13424	95610
1993	11872	5274	61806	19710	98662
1994	10162	4028	60618	19954	94763
1995	15056	3367	61207	21054	100684
1996	20833	7444	59648	20211	108136
1997	21229	7425	63125	20580	112359
1998	24222	6498	66761	23305	120787
1999	26429	9357	71087	23601	130474
2000	36714	12194	75479	25116	149503
2001	34908	11897	82179	26610	155595
2002	29906	9638	93336	31442	164323
2003	30276	12453	98673	32451	173853
2004	41559	13787	102656	34619	192621
2005	40990	12137	108668	36624	198418
*** Total ***	501546	167529	1066467	355702	2091243

AREA THREE TOTALS

YEAR	CROWN EXEMPT	FREEHOLD EXEMPT	NEW CROWN	NEW FREEHOLD	AREA THREE TOTAL
1987	22073	0	0	0	22073
1988	9933	0	9933	0	19865
1989	8392	0	17879	0	26271
1990	11748	0	16091	0	27839
1991	7574	2098	19580	0	29251
1992	18636	1888	22550	0	43074
1993	15073	0	21994	1699	38767
1994	10548	0	26578	1529	38655
1995	3389	0	30025	1376	34790
1996	7948	0	27022	1239	36209
1997	11431	0	27065	1115	39611
1998	10288	0	24358	1003	35650
1999	13540	0	25493	903	39937
2000	8235	0	28064	813	37112
2001	7412	0	25257	732	33400
2002	1215	742	28929	658	31544
2003	5873	667	26462	593	33595
2004	7424	0	23816	1134	32373
2005	4032	0	24083	1021	29136
*** Total ***	184764	5395	425177	13815	629151

NEW POOL ADDITIONS AREA FOUR

AREA FOUR TOTALS

YEAR	CROWN EXEMPT	FREEHOLD EXEMPT	NEW CROWN	NEW FREEHOLD	OLD CROWN	OLD FREEHOLD	AREA FOUR TOTAL
1987	11101	3700	0	0	0	0	14801
1988	19694	12826	0	0	0	0	32520
1989	40532	18337	6373	3187	0	0	68429
1990	41860	19028	16960	8595	0	0	86443
1991	35375	22610	35119	14204	0	0	107308
1992	29787	15449	49344	23788	0	0	118368
1993	23472	9395	59144	30494	0	0	122504
1994	16805	4559	64143	33790	0	0	119298
1995	19348	10129	70089	33626	0	0	133192
1996	25045	11492	69289	33026	0	0	138853
1997	29674	14159	74373	36592	0	0	154798
1998	27358	17470	80974	37882	0	0	163684
1999	27316	12593	85936	43706	0	0	169550
2000	35026	14446	90293	46434	0	0	186199
2001	30649	16559	96577	47815	0	0	191601
2002	29585	14800	105388	50312	0	0	200085
2003	30412	13327	109218	55274	0	0	208231
2004	29765	13519	114459	55276	0	0	213019
2005	30383	16162	117488	58480	0	0	222513
*** Total ***	533188	260561	1245166	612481	0	0	2651395

AREA FIVE TOTALS

YEAR	CROWN EXEMPT	FREEHOLD EXEMPT	NEW CROWN	NEW FREEHOLD	AREA FIVE TOTALS
1987	14801	6687	0	0	21488
1988	18976	9560	$2877	959	32371
1989	22667	10825	10798	5489	49778
1990	21344	10132	17937	8634	58047
1991	20793	10104	26036	13391	70324
1992	19780	11731	31837	15404	78751
1993	24919	13853	38439	18257	95467
1994	27261	12080	41200	22273	102814
1995	19402	9947	50601	26356	106306
1996	22459	11804	55857	28198	118318
1997	32924	17311	57461	29248	136945
1998	35626	21162	64285	30361	151434
1999	29536	13493	72706	38218	153953
2000	26689	13184	81534	42292	163699
2001	34985	18971	83242	42446	179644
2002	42011	19199	86213	45537	192959
2003	36565	18202	97045	48903	200715
2004	28814	14163	104725	53138	200839
2005	26381	11984	107866	55082	201314
*** Total ***	505932	254391	1030657	524187	2315167

NEW POOL ADDITIONS AREA SIX

AREA SIX TOTALS

YEAR	CROWN EXEMPT	FREEHOLD EXEMPT	NEW CROWN	NEW FREEHOLD	OLD CROWN	OLD FREEHOLD	TOTAL FOR AREA SIX	TOTAL FOR ALL AREAS
1987	51698	46494	0	0	0	0	98191	170494
1988	78677	73941	4736	4736	0	0	162090	302237
1989	78364	86157	42811	32610	0	0	239942	517506
1990	54903	56548	69074	63337	0	0	243862	620656
1991	44892	31070	94171	96776	0	0	266910	725964
1992	61913	43147	99063	99276	0	0	303399	810184
1993	46532	54250	110982	105870	0	0	317633	848607
1994	42503	39994	125394	117341	0	0	326932	856604
1995	25360	20716	130437	130374	0	0	306888	853226
1996	15387	17502	137181	130561	0	0	300631	868588
1997	17607	17321	127576	125118	0	0	287622	905086
1998	23374	20052	125220	118907	0	0	287554	937538
1999	25567	17946	120226	116402	0	0	280141	951161
2000	28856	26245	119749	112856	0	0	287706	1001651
2001	27267	29706	120145	109189	0	0	286307	1016373
2002	32729	25415	117659	113968	0	0	289771	1053335
2003	21448	28323	122072	112139	0	0	283982	1066264
2004	16520	16622	121950	114438	0	0	269531	1066186
2005	12691	8574	116757	114156	0	0	252178	1047710
*** Total ***	706389	660024	1906203	1818654	0	0	5091269	15619368

AREA ONE TOTALS

YEAR	CROWN EXEMPT	FREEHOLD EXEMPT	NEW CROWN	NEW FREEHOLD	CROWN EOR	FREEHOLD EOR	AREA ONE TOTAL
1987	75509	37857	0	0	0	0	113366
1988	84646	42278	29767	14698	0	0	171389
1989	87976	43754	59811	29350	0	0	220891
1990	86458	42768	90627	44564	0	0	264417
1991	82707	41340	115798	56464	0	0	296309
1992	80566	41045	140269	68687	0	0	330567
1993	80203	40410	157640	77710	0	0	355963
1994	78788	39464	174032	86290	0	0	378574
1995	77783	37935	187390	92584	0	0	395692
1996	72770	35483	198496	97383	0	0	404132
1997	62669	31760	209170	102208	0	0	405807
1998	52271	26634	212846	103190	0	0	394941
1999	43537	22262	213401	104621	0	0	383821
2000	36780	18739	207323	101035	0	0	363877
2001	31238	14947	201139	98666	0	0	345990
2002	25609	12195	190398	92779	0	0	320982
2003	20770	10391	181647	88018	0	0	300826
2004	17071	8367	168319	80885	0	0	274642
2005	13481	7040	157776	76034	0	0	254331
*** Total ***							
	1110833	554668	2895849	1415167	0	0	5976517

OLD POOL EXTENSIONS AREA TWO

AREA TWO TOTALS

YEAR	CROWN EXEMPT	FREEHOLD EXEMPT	NEW CROWN	NEW FREEHOLD	AREA TWO TOTAL
1987	36271	13265	0	0	49536
1988	55749	19541	12977	5017	93284
1989	67641	24446	30566	11179	133832
1990	69287	24352	57917	20695	172251
1991	72342	25641	82761	30022	210767
1992	75507	27022	107198	37962	247689
1993	79345	28352	130710	46908	285315
1994	83439	30390	153970	54764	322563
1995	86474	30564	177018	63424	357479
1996	88283	31313	200070	71761	391426
1997	87794	31828	222051	79206	420879
1998	86609	31210	243002	86863	447683
1999	84309	29981	261114	93571	468975
2000	80921	28847	277771	99502	487040
2001	78358	28350	291096	104120	501924
2002	75643	27810	302278	108163	513894
2003	73736	25845	311347	111636	522565
2004	70756	24746	318483	114588	528572
2005	66825	24356	324519	115859	531559
*** Total ***					
	1419288	507857	3504848	1255239	6687232

AREA THREE TOTALS

YEAR	CROWN EXEMPT	FREEHOLD EXEMPT	NEW CROWN	NEW FREEHOLD	AREA THREE TOTAL
1987	63367	6801	0	0	70168
1988	84610	10224	24540	2915	122288
1989	98998	13196	51327	5509	169029
1990	99534	12934	88411	10643	211521
1991	100968	12677	121763	15150	250559
1992	103661	12425	152235	19097	287418
1993	106267	12179	180412	22540	321398
1994	108618	13473	207276	25533	354899
1995	110654	14550	232210	28122	385537
1996	112538	14190	255874	31595	414196
1997	114792	13839	277720	34565	440916
1998	117364	13496	298413	37086	466359
1999	120012	14511	317935	39207	491665
2000	124045	15326	336779	40972	517122
2001	127382	16135	354737	43511	541765
2002	128632	16751	373268	45601	564252
2003	130449	16173	390516	48314	585452
2004	132111	15615	406539	50505	604770
2005	133749	16170	421982	52234	624135
*** Total ***	2117750	260664	4491939	553095	7423448

OLD POOL EXTENSIONS AREA FOUR

AREA FOUR TOTALS

YEAR	CROWN EXEMPT	FREEHOLD EXEMPT	NEW CROWN	NEW FREEHOLD	OLD CROWN	OLD FREEHOLD	AREA FOUR TOTAL
1987	173500	86529	0	0	0	0	260028
1988	212268	104356	70913	35571	0	0	423108
1989	228412	114050	149415	74517	0	0	566395
1990	218386	110244	243871	120503	0	0	693003
1991	209814	105248	325379	162391	0	0	802833
1992	200912	100458	398088	198715	0	0	898173
1993	190725	94687	460900	230487	0	0	976799
1994	180297	89524	515849	257644	0	0	1043313
1995	169941	85035	561169	280034	0	0	1096179
1996	159723	80276	599509	298975	0	0	1138484
1997	150476	75208	629620	314391	0	0	1169696
1998	140623	70322	653839	326606	0	0	1191390
1999	130903	65342	671806	335517	0	0	1203568
2000	121152	60849	684178	341828	0	0	1209007
2001	111598	55986	691280	345213	0	0	1204078
2002	102364	50917	693537	346779	0	0	1193597
2003	93213	46735	691426	345507	0	0	1176881
2004	84674	42544	685417	342490	0	0	1155125
2005	76701	38154	675718	337792	0	0	1128366
*** Total ***	2955680	1476466	9401915	4694962	0	0	18529024

AREA FIVE TOTALS

YEAR	CROWN EXEMPT	FREEHOLD EXEMPT	NEW CROWN	NEW FREEHOLD	AREA FIVE TOTALS
1987	58085	28784	0	0	86870
1988	53817	27417	29019	14175	124429
1989	61980	31543	47386	23344	164253
1990	64729	32786	67995	33810	199320
1991	63580	31737	89772	44946	230035
1992	62751	31282	108540	54318	256891
1993	61650	31055	125267	62571	280542
1994	60442	30554	140602	69912	301511
1995	59037	29790	152922	76521	318270
1996	58201	28917	164173	82155	333445
1997	56587	27913	173947	86935	345381
1998	52983	26810	182533	90831	353158
1999	50715	25942	188503	94078	359238
2000	48200	24337	193049	96564	362150
2001	45680	22885	196359	98246	363169
2002	43773	21854	198026	98964	362617
2003	41409	20570	198674	99404	360057
2004	38607	19442	198477	99171	355697
2005	36296	18171	197068	98424	349959
*** Total ***	1018522	511789	2652312	1324369	5506993

OLD POOL EXTENSIONS AREA SIX

AREA SIX TOTALS

YEAR	CROWN EXEMPT	FREEHOLD EXEMPT	NEW CROWN	NEW FREEHOLD	OLD CROWN	OLD FREEHOLD	TOTAL FOR AREA SIX	TOTAL FOR ALL AREAS
1987	139196	153750	0	0	0	0	292946	872913
1988	151181	168992	60258	65611	0	0	446043	1380541
1989	161827	179626	115268	127320	0	0	584041	1838442
1990	155209	171735	175093	194275	0	0	696312	2236825
1991	142805	158756	229462	254183	0	0	785206	2575707
1992	130492	145047	273523	303093	0	0	852155	2872893
1993	118916	131408	308275	341954	0	0	900552	3120569
1994	108136	119612	334565	371105	0	0	933417	3334277
1995	97677	108518	353756	391991	0	0	951943	3505099
1996	87804	97466	366600	406362	0	0	958232	3639917
1997	77866	87263	373832	414472	0	0	953233	3735910
1998	62999	77619	376039	417220	0	0	933878	3787409
1999	55053	68698	367224	415320	0	0	906295	3813562
2000	46384	60099	361380	409193	0	0	877056	3815251
2001	37656	51087	344688	396645	0	0	830076	3787002
2002	27843	34565	332531	376811	0	0	771750	3727091
2003	21464	26845	306040	355741	0	0	710091	3655872
2004	11248	16215	291090	320741	0	0	639295	3558101
2005	6519	10171	256670	285729	0	0	559089	3447440
*** Total ***	1640274	1867272	5226294	5847768	0	0	14581608	58704821

APPENDIX D

PLAY CATEGORIES AND NUMBER OF POOLS

CREATED BY THE
CANADIAN ENERGY RESEARCH INSTITUTE

129

Appendix D

PLAY CATEGORIES AND NUMBER OF POOLS

D.1 Plays Supplied to the Study

The Institute of Sedimentary and Petroleum Geology (ISPG) has
supplied play definitions and estimates of remaining pools to be
discovered in each play. The plays were divided into two classifications: heavy and light/medium. The heavy oil plays are provided
below.

D.1.1 Heavy Plays

Play Name	Area Class
Rex, Lloydminster, and Cummings	1
General Petroleums	1
Sparky	1
Colony, McLaren and Waseca	1
Bakken	2

The Rex, Lloydminster and Cummings play classification is within the Mannville group. This play is classified as occuring in Area 1
and ranges from 550 metres to 650 metres deep.

General Petroleums is also with the Mannville group and is
approximately 550 metres deep in Area 1. Above the General Petroleums
are the Sparky and Waseca, McLaren and Colony plays. These plays are
considered upper Mannville plays and occur as shallow as only 480
metres in this area.

The Bakken heavy oil play is a Devonian/Mississippian play and
is generally deeper than the Mannville--800 to 825 metres. Although
the Bakken is not restricted to Area 2 and the others are not restriced
to Area 1, we have chosen to classify these plays into these areas.
Since the exact location of the undiscovered pools is unknown, it is
difficult to accurately predict the area in which such pools will be
discovered.

The restriction of an entire play into one area greatly reduces the complexity of the modelling system.

D.1.2 Light/Medium Plays

Play Name	Area Class
Souris Valley - Tilston	6
Alida Frobisher	4
Midale Beds	4
Ratcliffe Structural	4
Lodgepole	0
Roseray Success Sandstone	3
Upper Shaunavon Sands/ Carbonates	3
Viking Sandstone, Saskatchewan	5
Basal Mannville Sands (Cantuar, Wapella)	3
Upper Devonian Stratigraphic/ Structural	6
Ratcliffe Stratigraphic	6

For a discussion of the light/medium plays see the ISPG publication, "Conventional Oil Resources of Western Canada (Light and Medium Gravity)," December, 1985.

APPENDIX E

ASSUMPTIONS AND RESULTS FROM
ACTIVITY MODEL

CREATED BY THE
CANADIAN ENERGY RESEARCH INSTITUTE

E.1

LOW CASE TABLES

TABLE E.1a

PRICE INPUT

Record#	AREA	YEAR	PROFIT	POIL	PGAS	ROYOIL	ROYGAS
1	1	1985	133.24	198.44	95.42	0.1600	0.1480
2	1	1986	33.98	87.09	98.90	0.1600	0.1570
3	1	1987	41.01	105.10	92.62	0.0470	0.2300
4	1	1988	21.20	54.34	56.65	0.0470	0.2300
5	1	1989	21.72	55.66	60.48	0.0530	0.2300
6	1	1990	22.45	57.55	65.93	0.0590	0.2300
7	1	1991	22.09	56.61	73.82	0.0670	0.2300
8	1	1992	24.15	61.89	80.36	0.0750	0.2300
9	1	1993	25.18	64.53	87.16	0.0830	0.2300
10	1	1994	26.33	67.49	97.27	0.0920	0.2030
11	1	1995	27.53	70.57	101.60	0.1020	0.2300
12	1	1996	28.64	73.40	105.66	0.1020	0.2300
13	1	1997	29.77	76.30	109.89	0.1020	0.2300
14	1	1998	30.97	79.38	114.29	0.1020	0.2300
15	1	1999	32.20	82.52	118.86	0.1020	0.2300
16	1	2000	33.50	85.86	123.61	0.1020	0.2300
17	1	2001	34.82	89.25	128.56	0.1020	0.2300
18	1	2002	36.22	92.84	133.70	0.1020	0.2300
19	1	2003	37.67	96.55	139.05	0.1020	0.2300
20	1	2004	39.19	100.45	144.61	0.1020	0.2300
21	1	2005	40.74	104.41	150.40	0.1020	0.2300
22	2	1985	204.17	199.58	0.00	0.2100	0.1480
23	2	1986	30.95	89.67	98.90	0.2200	0.1570
24	2	1987	36.56	105.92	92.62	0.1070	0.2300
25	2	1988	19.04	55.16	56.65	0.1070	0.2300
26	2	1989	19.30	55.92	60.48	0.1130	0.2300
27	2	1990	19.95	57.80	65.45	0.1190	0.2300
28	2	1991	20.58	59.63	73.82	0.1270	0.2300
29	2	1992	21.45	62.14	80.36	0.1350	0.2300
30	2	1993	22.38	64.85	87.16	0.1430	0.2300
31	2	1994	23.38	67.74	93.97	0.1520	0.2300
32	2	1995	24.44	70.82	101.60	0.1620	0.2300
33	2	1996	25.42	73.65	105.66	0.1620	0.2300
34	2	1997	26.42	76.55	109.89	0.1620	0.2300
35	2	1998	27.48	79.63	114.29	0.1620	0.2300
36	2	1999	28.59	82.84	118.86	0.1620	0.2300
37	2	2000	29.72	86.11	123.61	0.1620	0.2300
38	2	2001	30.92	89.57	128.56	0.1620	0.2300
39	2	2002	32.15	93.15	133.70	0.1620	0.2300
40	2	2003	33.43	96.86	139.05	0.1620	0.2300
41	2	2004	34.78	100.76	144.61	0.1620	0.2300
42	2	2005	36.17	104.79	150.40	0.1620	0.2300
43	3	1985	32.55	187.06	95.42	0.3000	0.1480
44	3	1986	10.76	100.56	98.90	0.3100	0.1570
45	3	1987	12.86	120.20	92.62	0.2190	0.2300
46	3	1988	6.55	61.20	56.65	0.2190	0.2300
47	3	1989	6.67	62.33	60.48	0.2250	0.2300
48	3	1990	6.86	64.09	65.93	0.2310	0.2300
49	3	1991	7.03	65.67	73.82	0.2380	0.2300
50	3	1992	7.27	67.99	80.36	0.2450	0.2300
51	3	1993	7.54	70.51	87.16	0.2530	0.2300
52	3	1994	7.83	73.21	93.97	0.2610	0.2300
53	3	1995	8.15	76.17	101.60	0.2690	0.2300
54	3	1996	8.47	79.19	105.66	0.2690	0.2300
55	3	1997	8.81	82.33	109.89	0.2690	0.2300
56	3	1998	9.17	85.67	114.29	0.2690	0.2300
57	3	1999	9.53	89.06	118.86	0.2690	0.2300
58	3	2000	9.91	92.65	123.61	0.2690	0.2300
59	3	2001	10.31	96.36	128.56	0.2690	0.2300
60	3	2002	10.72	100.20	133.70	0.2690	0.2300
61	3	2003	11.15	104.22	139.05	0.2690	0.2300
62	3	2004	11.60	108.37	144.61	0.2690	0.2300

Continued on Next Page

(TABLE E.1a continued)

63	3	2005	12.06	112.71	150.40	0.2690	0.2300
64	4	1985	104.28	207.82	95.42	0.2500	0.1480
65	4	1986	78.86	107.61	98.90	0.2600	0.1570
66	4	1987	94.17	128.50	92.62	0.2010	0.2300
67	4	1988	47.29	64.53	56.65	0.2010	0.2300
68	4	1989	49.64	67.74	60.48	0.2070	0.2300
69	4	1990	51.72	70.57	65.93	0.2130	0.2300
70	4	1991	54.11	73.84	73.82	0.2190	0.2300
71	4	1992	56.37	76.92	80.36	0.2260	0.2300
72	4	1993	58.82	80.26	87.16	0.2320	0.2300
73	4	1994	61.40	83.78	93.97	0.2390	0.2300
74	4	1995	64.03	87.37	101.60	0.2460	0.2300
75	4	1996	66.56	90.83	105.66	0.2460	0.2300
76	4	1997	69.23	94.47	109.89	0.2460	0.2300
77	4	1998	72.00	98.25	114.29	0.2460	0.2300
78	4	1999	74.90	102.21	118.86	0.2460	0.2300
79	4	2000	77.90	106.30	123.61	0.2460	0.2300
80	4	2001	80.99	110.51	128.56	0.2460	0.2300
81	4	2002	84.26	114.98	133.70	0.2460	0.2300
82	4	2003	87.62	119.57	139.05	0.2460	0.2300
83	4	2004	91.13	124.35	144.61	0.2460	0.2300
84	4	2005	94.77	129.32	150.40	0.2460	0.2300
85	5	1985	204.17	241.16	95.42	0.0800	0.1480
86	5	1986	30.15	121.64	98.90	0.0800	0.1570
87	5	1987	35.81	144.48	92.62	0.0180	0.2300
88	5	1988	17.73	71.52	56.65	0.0180	0.2300
89	5	1989	18.49	74.60	60.48	0.0185	0.2300
90	5	1990	19.14	77.24	65.93	0.0188	0.2300
91	5	1991	19.89	80.26	73.82	0.0191	0.2300
92	5	1992	20.61	83.15	80.36	0.0194	0.2300
93	5	1993	21.39	86.30	87.16	0.0197	0.2300
94	5	1994	22.22	89.63	93.97	0.0200	0.2300
95	5	1995	23.07	93.09	101.60	0.0203	0.2300
96	5	1996	23.99	96.80	105.66	0.0203	0.2300
97	5	1997	24.94	100.64	109.89	0.0203	0.2300
98	5	1998	25.94	104.66	114.29	0.0203	0.2300
99	5	1999	26.99	108.88	118.86	0.0203	0.2300
100	5	2000	28.06	113.22	123.61	0.0203	0.2300
101	5	2001	29.19	117.75	128.56	0.0203	0.2300
102	5	2002	30.35	122.46	133.70	0.0203	0.2300
103	5	2003	31.57	127.37	139.05	0.0203	0.2300
104	5	2004	32.83	132.46	144.61	0.0203	0.2300
105	5	2005	34.16	137.81	150.40	0.0203	0.2300
106	6	1985	140.80	210.97	95.42	0.2500	0.1480
107	6	1986	78.86	117.80	98.90	0.2600	0.1570
108	6	1987	93.56	139.76	94.43	0.1760	0.2300
109	6	1988	46.65	69.69	56.65	0.1760	0.2300
110	6	1989	48.55	72.52	60.48	0.1800	0.2300
111	6	1990	50.36	75.23	65.93	0.1850	0.2300
112	6	1991	52.46	78.37	73.82	0.1890	0.2300
113	6	1992	54.45	81.33	80.36	0.1930	0.2300
114	6	1993	56.55	84.47	87.16	0.1980	0.2300
115	6	1994	58.82	87.87	93.97	0.2020	0.2300
116	6	1995	61.18	91.39	101.60	0.2070	0.2300
117	6	1996	63.62	95.04	105.66	0.2070	0.2300
118	6	1997	66.15	98.81	109.89	0.2070	0.2300
119	6	1998	68.81	102.78	114.29	0.2070	0.2300
120	6	1999	71.54	106.86	118.86	0.2070	0.2300
121	6	2000	74.40	111.14	123.61	0.2070	0.2300
122	6	2001	77.39	115.61	128.56	0.2070	0.2300
123	6	2002	80.47	120.20	133.70	0.2070	0.2300
124	6	2003	83.71	125.04	139.05	0.2070	0.2300
125	6	2004	87.03	130.01	144.61	0.2070	0.2300
126	6	2005	90.53	135.23	921.72	0.2070	0.2300

TABLE E.1b

COST INPUT

Record#	AREA	YEAR	SUCCESS	OPCOST	DRILLCOST	EWEIGHT	SWEIGHT	DUP	DUF
1	1	1985	0.820	38.81	1253.00	1.00	0.50	1.00	1.00
2	1	1986	0.750	34.91	1127.70	1.00	0.50	1.00	1.00
3	1	1987	0.720	34.91	1127.70	1.00	0.50	1.00	1.00
4	1	1988	0.720	36.29	1172.81	1.00	0.50	1.00	1.00
5	1	1989	0.720	37.74	1219.72	1.00	0.50	1.00	1.00
6	1	1990	0.720	39.25	1268.51	1.00	0.50	1.00	1.00
7	1	1991	0.720	40.82	1319.25	1.00	0.50	1.00	1.00
8	1	1992	0.720	42.46	1372.02	1.00	0.50	1.00	1.00
9	1	1993	0.720	44.15	1426.90	1.00	0.50	1.00	1.00
10	1	1994	0.720	45.92	1483.98	1.00	0.50	1.00	1.00
11	1	1995	0.720	47.74	1543.34	1.00	0.50	1.00	1.00
12	1	1996	0.700	49.63	1605.07	1.00	0.50	1.00	1.00
13	1	1997	0.680	51.64	1669.27	1.00	0.50	1.00	1.00
14	1	1998	0.660	53.72	1736.04	1.00	0.50	1.00	1.00
15	1	1999	0.640	55.85	1805.48	1.00	0.50	1.00	1.00
16	1	2000	0.620	58.12	1877.70	1.00	0.50	1.00	1.00
17	1	2001	0.600	60.45	1952.81	1.00	0.50	1.00	1.00
18	1	2002	0.580	62.84	2030.92	1.00	0.50	1.00	1.00
19	1	2003	0.560	65.35	2112.16	1.00	0.50	1.00	1.00
20	1	2004	0.540	67.99	2196.65	1.00	0.50	1.00	1.00
21	1	2005	0.520	70.70	2284.51	1.00	0.50	1.00	1.00
22	2	1985	0.960	32.02	1366.30	0.75	0.50	1.00	1.00
23	2	1986	0.940	28.81	1229.94	0.75	0.50	1.00	1.00
24	2	1987	0.790	28.81	1229.94	0.75	0.50	1.00	1.00
25	2	1988	0.790	29.94	1279.14	0.75	0.50	1.00	1.00
26	2	1989	0.790	31.13	1330.30	0.75	0.50	1.00	1.00
27	2	1990	0.790	32.39	1383.52	0.75	0.50	1.00	1.00
28	2	1991	0.790	33.71	1438.86	0.75	0.50	1.00	1.00
29	2	1992	0.790	35.03	1496.41	0.75	0.50	1.00	1.00
30	2	1993	0.790	36.42	1556.27	0.75	0.50	1.00	1.00
31	2	1994	0.790	37.86	1618.52	0.75	0.50	1.00	1.00
32	2	1995	0.790	39.37	1683.26	0.75	0.50	1.00	1.00
33	2	1996	0.770	40.95	1750.59	0.75	0.50	1.00	1.00
34	2	1997	0.750	42.58	1820.61	0.75	0.50	1.00	1.00
35	2	1998	0.730	44.28	1893.44	0.75	0.50	1.00	1.00
36	2	1999	0.710	46.04	1969.17	0.75	0.50	1.00	1.00
37	2	2000	0.690	47.87	2047.94	0.75	0.50	1.00	1.00
38	2	2001	0.670	49.75	2129.86	0.75	0.50	1.00	1.00
39	2	2002	0.650	51.77	2215.05	0.75	0.50	1.00	1.00
40	2	2003	0.630	53.84	2303.65	0.75	0.50	1.00	1.00
41	2	2004	0.610	55.98	2395.80	0.75	0.50	1.00	1.00
42	2	2005	0.590	58.24	2491.63	0.75	0.50	1.00	1.00
43	3	1985	0.670	23.46	1667.50	0.50	0.50	1.20	1.00
44	3	1986	0.590	21.13	1500.76	0.50	0.50	1.20	1.00
45	3	1987	0.590	21.13	1500.76	0.50	0.50	1.20	1.00
46	3	1988	0.590	21.95	1560.79	0.50	0.50	1.20	1.00
47	3	1989	0.590	22.83	1623.22	0.50	0.50	1.20	1.00
48	3	1990	0.590	23.78	1688.15	0.50	0.50	1.20	1.00
49	3	1991	0.590	24.72	1755.68	0.50	0.50	1.20	1.00
50	3	1992	0.590	25.73	1825.90	0.50	0.50	1.20	1.00
51	3	1993	0.590	26.73	1898.94	0.50	0.50	1.20	1.00
52	3	1994	0.590	27.80	1974.90	0.50	0.50	1.20	1.00
53	3	1995	0.590	28.93	2053.89	0.50	0.50	1.20	1.00
54	3	1996	0.570	30.07	2136.05	0.50	0.50	1.20	1.00
55	3	1997	0.550	31.26	2221.49	0.50	0.50	1.20	1.00
56	3	1998	0.530	32.52	2310.35	0.50	0.50	1.20	1.00
57	3	1999	0.510	33.84	2402.77	0.50	0.50	1.20	1.00
58	3	2000	0.490	35.22	2498.88	0.50	0.50	1.20	1.00
59	3	2001	0.470	36.61	2598.83	0.50	0.50	1.20	1.00
60	3	2002	0.450	38.05	2702.78	0.50	0.50	1.20	1.00
61	3	2003	0.430	39.56	2810.90	0.50	0.50	1.20	1.00
62	3	2004	0.410	41.14	2923.33	0.50	0.50	1.20	1.00
63	3	2005	0.390	42.77	3040.26	0.50	0.50	1.20	1.00

Continued on Next Page

138

(TABLE E.1b continued)

63	3 2005	0.390	42.77	3040.26	0.50	0.50	1.20	1.00
64	4 1985	0.800	30.76	2217.90	1.00	0.50	1.50	1.00
65	4 1986	0.765	27.68	1996.11	1.00	0.50	1.20	1.00
66	4 1987	0.710	27.68	1996.11	1.00	0.50	1.20	1.00
67	4 1988	0.710	28.81	2075.95	1.00	0.50	1.20	1.00
68	4 1989	0.710	29.94	2158.99	1.00	0.50	1.20	1.00
69	4 1990	0.710	31.13	2245.35	1.00	0.50	1.20	1.00
70	4 1991	0.710	32.39	2335.17	1.00	0.50	1.20	1.00
71	4 1992	0.710	33.71	2428.57	1.00	0.50	1.20	1.00
72	4 1993	0.710	35.03	2525.72	1.00	0.50	1.20	1.00
73	4 1994	0.710	36.42	2626.74	1.00	0.50	1.20	1.00
74	4 1995	0.710	37.86	2731.81	1.00	0.50	1.20	1.00
75	4 1996	0.690	39.37	2841.09	1.00	0.50	1.20	1.00
76	4 1997	0.670	40.95	2954.73	1.00	0.50	1.20	1.00
77	4 1998	0.650	42.58	3072.92	1.00	0.50	1.20	1.00
78	4 1999	0.630	44.28	3195.84	1.00	0.50	1.20	1.00
79	4 2000	0.610	46.04	3323.67	1.00	0.50	1.20	1.00
80	4 2001	0.590	47.87	3456.62	1.00	0.50	1.20	1.00
81	4 2002	0.570	49.75	3594.88	1.00	0.50	1.20	1.00
82	4 2003	0.550	51.77	3738.68	1.00	0.50	1.20	1.00
83	4 2004	0.530	53.84	3888.22	1.00	0.50	1.20	1.00
84	4 2005	0.510	55.98	4043.75	1.00	0.50	1.20	1.00
85	5 1985	0.960	28.74	1017.20	0.50	0.50	0.70	1.00
86	5 1986	0.940	25.85	915.48	0.50	0.50	0.40	1.00
87	5 1987	0.940	25.85	915.48	0.50	0.50	0.40	1.00
88	5 1988	0.940	26.86	952.10	0.50	0.50	0.40	1.00
89	5 1989	0.940	27.93	990.18	0.50	0.50	0.40	1.00
90	5 1990	0.940	29.06	1029.79	0.50	0.50	0.40	1.00
91	5 1991	0.940	30.19	1070.98	0.50	0.50	0.40	1.00
92	5 1992	0.940	31.39	1113.82	0.50	0.50	0.40	1.00
93	5 1993	0.940	32.64	1158.37	0.50	0.50	0.40	1.00
94	5 1994	0.940	33.97	1204.71	0.50	0.50	0.40	1.00
95	5 1995	0.940	35.35	1252.90	0.50	0.50	0.40	1.00
96	5 1996	0.920	36.73	1303.01	0.50	0.50	0.40	1.00
97	5 1997	0.900	38.18	1355.13	0.50	0.50	0.40	1.00
98	5 1998	0.880	39.69	1409.34	0.50	0.50	0.40	1.00
99	5 1999	0.860	41.26	1465.71	0.50	0.50	0.40	1.00
100	5 2000	0.840	42.90	1524.34	0.50	0.50	0.40	1.00
101	5 2001	0.820	44.59	1585.32	0.50	0.50	0.40	1.00
102	5 2002	0.800	46.36	1648.73	0.50	0.50	0.40	1.00
103	5 2003	0.780	48.18	1714.68	0.50	0.50	0.40	1.00
104	5 2004	0.760	50.13	1783.26	0.50	0.50	0.40	1.00
105	5 2005	0.740	52.14	1854.59	0.50	0.50	0.40	1.00
106	6 1985	0.800	33.08	1912.50	0.50	0.50	1.75	1.00
107	6 1986	0.710	29.75	1721.25	0.50	0.50	1.40	1.00
108	6 1987	0.710	29.75	1721.25	0.50	0.50	1.40	1.00
109	6 1988	0.710	30.95	1790.10	0.50	0.50	1.40	1.00
110	6 1989	0.710	32.20	1861.70	0.50	0.50	1.40	1.00
111	6 1990	0.710	33.46	1936.17	0.50	0.50	1.40	1.00
112	6 1991	0.710	34.78	2013.62	0.50	0.50	1.40	1.00
113	6 1992	0.710	36.17	2094.16	0.50	0.50	1.40	1.00
114	6 1993	0.710	37.61	2177.93	0.50	0.50	1.40	1.00
115	6 1994	0.710	39.12	2265.05	0.50	0.50	1.40	1.00
116	6 1995	0.710	40.70	2355.65	0.50	0.50	1.40	1.00
117	6 1996	0.690	42.33	2449.88	0.50	0.50	1.40	1.00
118	6 1997	0.670	44.03	2547.87	0.50	0.50	1.40	1.00
119	6 1998	0.650	45.79	2649.79	0.50	0.50	1.40	1.00
120	6 1999	0.630	47.61	2755.78	0.50	0.50	1.40	1.00
121	6 2000	0.610	49.50	2866.01	0.50	0.50	1.40	1.00
122	6 2001	0.590	51.45	2980.65	0.50	0.50	1.40	1.00
123	6 2002	0.570	53.53	3099.88	0.50	0.50	1.40	1.00
124	6 2003	0.550	55.66	3223.87	0.50	0.50	1.40	1.00
125	6 2004	0.530	57.87	3352.82	0.50	0.50	1.40	1.00
126	6 2005	0.510	60.19	3486.94	0.50	0.50	1.40	1.00

TABLE E.1c

RESULTS

Record#	AREA	YEAR	WELLS	CWELLS	SEWELLS	DWELLS	SDWELLS	EORWELL
1	1	1985	0	0	0	0	0	0.0
2	1	1986	98	14	0	84	61	6.7
3	1	1987	114	16	1	98	71	7.9
4	1	1988	21	3	0	18	13	1.4
5	1	1989	20	3	0	17	12	1.4
6	1	1990	20	3	0	17	12	1.4
7	1	1991	16	2	1	14	10	1.1
8	1	1992	19	3	0	16	12	1.3
9	1	1993	19	3	0	16	12	1.3
10	1	1994	19	3	0	16	12	1.3
11	1	1995	19	3	0	16	12	1.3
12	1	1996	18	3	0	15	11	1.2
13	1	1997	16	2	0	14	10	1.1
14	1	1998	13	2	1	11	8	0.9
15	1	1999	11	2	0	9	7	0.7
16	1	2000	10	1	0	9	7	0.7
17	1	2001	8	1	0	7	5	0.6
18	1	2002	7	1	0	6	4	0.5
19	1	2003	6	1	0	5	4	0.4
20	1	2004	5	1	0	4	3	0.3
21	1	2005	4	1	0	3	2	0.2
22	2	1985	0	0	0	0	0	0.0
23	2	1986	31	3	0	28	22	0.0
24	2	1987	44	5	0	39	30	0.0
25	2	1988	5	1	0	4	3	0.0
26	2	1989	5	1	0	4	3	0.0
27	2	1990	5	1	0	4	3	0.0
28	2	1991	5	1	1	4	3	0.0
29	2	1992	5	1	0	4	3	0.0
30	2	1993	5	1	0	4	3	0.0
31	2	1994	6	1	0	5	4	0.0
32	2	1995	6	1	0	5	4	0.0
33	2	1996	6	1	0	5	4	0.0
34	2	1997	6	1	0	5	4	0.0
35	2	1998	6	1	0	5	4	0.0
36	2	1999	6	1	0	5	4	0.0
37	2	2000	6	1	0	5	4	0.0
38	2	2001	5	1	0	4	3	0.0
39	2	2002	5	1	0	4	3	0.0
40	2	2003	5	1	0	4	3	0.0
41	2	2004	5	1	0	4	3	0.0
42	2	2005	5	1	0	4	3	0.0
43	3	1985	0	0	0	0	0	0.0
44	3	1986	27	3	0	24	14	1.6
45	3	1987	29	3	1	26	16	1.7
46	3	1988	14	2	0	12	7	0.8
47	3	1989	12	1	0	11	7	0.7
48	3	1990	12	1	0	11	7	0.7
49	3	1991	12	1	0	11	7	0.7
50	3	1992	12	1	0	11	7	0.7
51	3	1993	12	1	0	11	7	0.7
52	3	1994	12	1	0	11	7	0.7
53	3	1995	13	2	0	11	7	0.7
54	3	1996	13	2	0	11	7	0.7
55	3	1997	14	2	0	12	7	0.8
56	3	1998	14	2	0	12	7	0.8
57	3	1999	15	2	0	13	8	0.9
58	3	2000	15	2	0	13	8	0.9
59	3	2001	16	2	1	14	8	0.9
60	3	2002	16	2	0	14	8	0.9
61	3	2003	17	2	0	15	9	1.0
62	3	2004	18	2	0	16	10	1.1
63	3	2005	18	2	0	16	10	1.1

(Continued on Next Page)

(TABLE E.1c continued)

64	4 1985	0	0	0	0	0	0.0
65	4 1986	139	18	1	121	91	0.0
66	4 1987	172	22	1	150	113	0.0
67	4 1988	84	11	1	73	55	0.0
68	4 1989	87	11	0	76	57	0.0
69	4 1990	89	12	1	77	58	0.0
70	4 1991	92	12	0	80	60	0.0
71	4 1992	93	12	1	81	61	0.0
72	4 1993	96	12	0	84	63	0.0
73	4 1994	98	13	1	85	64	0.0
74	4 1995	100	13	1	87	65	0.0
75	4 1996	103	13	0	90	68	0.0
76	4 1997	105	14	1	91	68	0.0
77	4 1998	108	14	1	94	71	0.0
78	4 1999	111	14	1	97	73	0.0
79	4 2000	115	15	0	100	75	0.0
80	4 2001	118	15	1	103	77	0.0
81	4 2002	121	16	1	105	79	0.0
82	4 2003	124	16	1	108	81	0.0
83	4 2004	128	17	0	111	83	0.0
84	4 2005	131	17	1	114	86	0.0
85	5 1985	0	0	0	0	0	0.0
86	5 1986	143	16	1	127	98	0.0
87	5 1987	105	12	1	93	72	0.0
88	5 1988	67	7	0	60	46	0.0
89	5 1989	58	6	0	52	40	0.0
90	5 1990	60	7	1	53	41	0.0
91	5 1991	62	7	0	55	42	0.0
92	5 1992	63	7	0	56	43	0.0
93	5 1993	65	7	1	58	45	0.0
94	5 1994	67	7	0	60	46	0.0
95	5 1995	69	8	1	61	47	0.0
96	5 1996	71	8	0	63	48	0.0
97	5 1997	72	8	0	64	49	0.0
98	5 1998	73	8	1	65	50	0.0
99	5 1999	75	8	0	67	52	0.0
100	5 2000	76	8	1	68	52	0.0
101	5 2001	77	9	0	68	52	0.0
102	5 2002	78	9	0	69	53	0.0
103	5 2003	79	9	1	70	54	0.0
104	5 2004	81	9	0	72	55	0.0
105	5 2005	82	9	1	73	56	0.0
106	6 1985	0	0	0	0	0	0.0
107	6 1986	216	18	1	198	149	0.0
108	6 1987	239	20	1	219	164	0.0
109	6 1988	118	10	0	108	81	0.0
110	6 1989	101	9	1	92	69	0.0
111	6 1990	103	9	0	94	71	0.0
112	6 1991	106	9	1	97	73	0.0
113	6 1992	108	9	0	99	74	0.0
114	6 1993	110	9	0	101	76	0.0
115	6 1994	112	10	1	102	77	0.0
116	6 1995	114	10	0	104	78	0.0
117	6 1996	118	10	1	108	81	0.0
118	6 1997	121	10	0	111	83	0.0
119	6 1998	124	11	1	113	85	0.0
120	6 1999	128	11	1	117	88	0.0
121	6 2000	131	11	0	120	90	0.0
122	6 2001	135	11	1	124	93	0.0
123	6 2002	138	12	0	126	95	0.0
124	6 2003	142	12	1	130	98	0.0
125	6 2004	146	12	0	134	101	0.0
126	6 2005	150	13	1	137	103	0.0

E.2

BASE CASE TABLES

TABLE E.2a

PRICE INPUT

Record#	AREA	YEAR	PROFIT	POIL	PGAS	ROYOIL	ROYGAS
1	1	1985	213.72	198.44	66.02	0.1600	0.1480
2	1	1986	33.98	87.09	98.90	0.1600	0.1570
3	1	1987	41.10	105.35	92.62	0.0470	0.2300
4	1	1988	45.72	117.18	56.65	0.0470	0.2300
5	1	1989	46.92	120.26	60.48	0.0530	0.2300
6	1	1990	49.70	127.37	65.93	0.0590	0.2300
7	1	1991	50.04	128.25	73.82	0.0670	0.2300
8	1	1992	57.11	146.36	80.36	0.0750	0.2300
9	1	1993	60.98	156.30	87.16	0.0830	0.2300
10	1	1994	65.89	168.88	97.27	0.0920	0.2030
11	1	1995	71.22	182.53	101.60	0.1020	0.2300
12	1	1996	73.75	189.01	105.66	0.1020	0.2300
13	1	1997	77.11	197.63	109.89	0.1020	0.2300
14	1	1998	79.95	204.92	114.29	0.1020	0.2300
15	1	1999	82.92	212.53	118.86	0.1020	0.2300
16	1	2000	86.09	220.65	123.61	0.1020	0.2300
17	1	2001	90.16	231.09	128.56	0.1020	0.2300
18	1	2002	93.72	240.21	133.70	0.1020	0.2300
19	1	2003	97.45	249.77	139.05	0.1020	0.2300
20	1	2004	101.41	259.90	144.61	0.1020	0.2300
21	1	2005	104.76	268.51	150.40	0.1020	0.2300
22	2	1985	74.98	199.58	66.02	0.2100	0.1480
23	2	1986	33.68	89.67	98.90	0.2200	0.1570
24	2	1987	39.85	106.11	92.62	0.1070	0.2300
25	2	1988	44.67	118.94	56.65	0.1070	0.2300
26	2	1989	45.41	120.89	60.48	0.1130	0.2300
27	2	1990	48.08	128.00	65.93	0.1190	0.2300
28	2	1991	50.77	135.17	73.82	0.1270	0.2300
29	2	1992	55.19	146.93	80.36	0.1350	0.2300
30	2	1993	58.94	156.93	87.16	0.1430	0.2300
31	2	1994	63.67	169.51	93.97	0.1520	0.2300
32	2	1995	68.79	183.16	101.60	0.1620	0.2300
33	2	1996	71.23	189.64	105.66	0.1620	0.2300
34	2	1997	74.49	198.32	109.89	0.1620	0.2300
35	2	1998	77.23	205.61	114.29	0.1620	0.2300
36	2	1999	80.11	213.29	118.86	0.1620	0.2300
37	2	2000	83.16	221.40	123.61	0.1620	0.2300
38	2	2001	87.13	231.97	128.56	0.1620	0.2300
39	2	2002	90.53	241.03	133.70	0.1620	0.2300
40	2	2003	93.81	249.77	139.05	0.1620	0.2300
41	2	2004	97.62	259.90	144.61	0.1620	0.2300
42	2	2005	100.85	268.51	150.40	0.1620	0.2300
43	3	1985	32.55	187.06	66.02	0.3000	0.1480
44	3	1986	10.76	100.56	98.90	0.3100	0.1570
45	3	1987	12.86	120.45	92.62	0.2190	0.2300
46	3	1988	19.64	131.90	56.65	0.2190	0.2300
47	3	1989	20.41	134.79	60.48	0.2250	0.2300
48	3	1990	21.37	141.90	65.93	0.2310	0.2300
49	3	1991	22.33	148.88	73.82	0.2380	0.2300
50	3	1992	23.56	160.83	80.36	0.2450	0.2300
51	3	1993	24.89	170.64	87.16	0.2530	0.2300
52	3	1994	26.36	183.29	93.97	0.2610	0.2300
53	3	1995	27.92	196.93	101.60	0.2690	0.2300
54	3	1996	29.60	203.98	105.66	0.2690	0.2300
55	3	1997	31.38	213.29	109.89	0.2690	0.2300
56	3	1998	33.26	221.09	114.29	0.2690	0.2300
57	3	1999	35.25	229.39	118.86	0.2690	0.2300
58	3	2000	37.37	238.13	123.61	0.2690	0.2300
59	3	2001	39.61	249.39	128.56	0.2690	0.2300
60	3	2002	41.99	259.20	133.70	0.2690	0.2300
61	3	2003	44.51	269.52	139.05	0.2690	0.2300
62	3	2004	47.18	280.40	144.61	0.2690	0.2300

Continued on Next Page

(TABLE E.2a continued)

63	3	2005	50.01	289.77	150.40	0.2690	0.2300
64	4	1985	65.62	207.82	66.02	0.2500	0.1480
65	4	1986	33.98	107.61	98.90	0.2600	0.1570
66	4	1987	40.64	128.69	92.62	0.2010	0.2300
67	4	1988	43.93	139.13	56.65	0.2010	0.2300
68	4	1989	46.24	146.43	60.48	0.2070	0.2300
69	4	1990	49.32	156.18	65.93	0.2130	0.2300
70	4	1991	52.85	167.37	73.82	0.2190	0.2300
71	4	1992	57.44	181.90	80.36	0.2260	0.2300
72	4	1993	61.35	194.29	87.16	0.2320	0.2300
73	4	1994	66.20	209.64	93.97	0.2390	0.2300
74	4	1995	71.36	225.99	101.60	0.2460	0.2300
75	4	1996	73.88	233.98	105.66	0.2460	0.2300
76	4	1997	77.26	244.67	109.89	0.2460	0.2300
77	4	1998	80.10	253.67	114.29	0.2460	0.2300
78	4	1999	83.10	263.17	118.86	0.2460	0.2300
79	4	2000	86.28	273.23	123.61	0.2460	0.2300
80	4	2001	90.37	286.19	128.56	0.2460	0.2300
81	4	2002	93.90	297.38	133.70	0.2460	0.2300
82	4	2003	97.66	309.27	139.05	0.2460	0.2300
83	4	2004	101.59	321.72	144.61	0.2460	0.2300
84	4	2005	104.97	332.42	150.40	0.2460	0.2300
85	5	1985	67.38	241.16	66.02	0.0800	0.1480
86	5	1986	33.98	121.64	98.90	0.0800	0.1570
87	5	1987	40.43	144.73	92.62	0.0180	0.2300
88	5	1988	43.06	154.16	56.65	0.0180	0.2300
89	5	1989	45.02	161.15	60.48	0.0185	0.2300
90	5	1990	47.76	170.96	65.93	0.0188	0.2300
91	5	1991	50.83	181.96	73.82	0.0191	0.2300
92	5	1992	54.93	196.62	80.36	0.0194	0.2300
93	5	1993	58.35	208.89	87.16	0.0197	0.2300
94	5	1994	62.64	224.23	93.97	0.0200	0.2300
95	5	1995	67.26	240.77	101.60	0.0203	0.2300
96	5	1996	69.65	249.33	105.66	0.0203	0.2300
97	5	1997	72.83	260.71	109.89	0.0203	0.2300
98	5	1998	75.48	270.21	114.29	0.0203	0.2300
99	5	1999	78.33	280.40	118.86	0.0203	0.2300
100	5	2000	81.32	291.09	123.61	0.0203	0.2300
101	5	2001	85.17	304.87	128.56	0.0203	0.2300
102	5	2002	88.50	316.82	133.70	0.0203	0.2300
103	5	2003	92.03	329.46	139.05	0.0203	0.2300
104	5	2004	95.74	342.73	144.61	0.0203	0.2300
105	5	2005	98.94	354.18	150.40	0.0203	0.2300
106	6	1985	60.77	210.95	66.02	0.2500	0.1480
107	6	1986	33.98	117.80	98.90	0.2600	0.1570
108	6	1987	40.39	140.01	94.43	0.1760	0.2300
109	6	1988	43.34	150.26	56.65	0.1760	0.2300
110	6	1989	45.23	156.81	60.48	0.1800	0.2300
111	6	1990	48.04	166.55	65.93	0.1850	0.2300
112	6	1991	51.22	177.56	73.82	0.1890	0.2300
113	6	1992	55.45	192.22	80.36	0.1930	0.2300
114	6	1993	59.00	204.55	87.16	0.1980	0.2300
115	6	1994	63.41	219.83	93.97	0.2020	0.2300
116	6	1995	68.18	236.37	101.60	0.2070	0.2300
117	6	1996	70.60	244.74	105.66	0.2070	0.2300
118	6	1997	73.81	255.87	109.89	0.2070	0.2300
119	6	1998	76.53	265.30	114.29	0.2070	0.2300
120	6	1999	79.39	275.24	118.86	0.2070	0.2300
121	6	2000	82.43	285.75	123.61	0.2070	0.2300
122	6	2001	86.33	299.27	128.56	0.2070	0.2300
123	6	2002	89.72	311.03	133.70	0.2070	0.2300
124	6	2003	93.29	323.42	139.05	0.2070	0.2300
125	6	2004	97.07	336.51	144.61	0.2070	0.2300
126	6	2005	100.30	347.70	921.72	0.2070	0.2300

TABLE E.2b

COST INPUT

Record#	AREA	YEAR	SUCCESS	OPCOST	DRILLCOST	EWEIGHT	SWEIGHT	DUP	DUF
1	1	1985	0.820	38.81	1253.00	1.00	0.50	1.00	1.00
2	1	1986	0.750	34.92	1127.70	1.00	0.50	1.00	1.00
3	1	1987	0.720	34.92	1127.70	1.00	0.50	1.00	1.00
4	1	1988	0.720	38.84	1254.33	1.00	0.50	1.00	1.00
5	1	1989	0.720	39.86	1287.30	1.00	0.50	1.00	1.00
6	1	1990	0.720	42.22	1363.41	1.00	0.50	1.00	1.00
7	1	1991	0.720	42.51	1372.83	1.00	0.50	1.00	1.00
8	1	1992	0.720	48.51	1566.68	1.00	0.50	1.00	1.00
9	1	1993	0.720	51.81	1673.09	1.00	0.50	1.00	1.00
10	1	1994	0.720	55.98	1807.75	1.00	0.50	1.00	1.00
11	1	1995	0.720	60.50	1953.86	1.00	0.50	1.00	1.00
12	1	1996	0.700	62.65	2023.22	1.00	0.50	1.00	1.00
13	1	1997	0.680	65.51	2115.49	1.00	0.50	1.00	1.00
14	1	1998	0.660	67.92	2193.53	1.00	0.50	1.00	1.00
15	1	1999	0.640	70.45	2274.99	1.00	0.50	1.00	1.00
16	1	2000	0.620	73.14	2361.91	1.00	0.50	1.00	1.00
17	1	2001	0.600	76.60	2473.66	1.00	0.50	1.00	1.00
18	1	2002	0.580	79.62	2571.28	1.00	0.50	1.00	1.00
19	1	2003	0.560	82.79	2673.62	1.00	0.50	1.00	1.00
20	1	2004	0.540	86.15	2782.05	1.00	0.50	1.00	1.00
21	1	2005	0.520	89.00	2874.22	1.00	0.50	1.00	1.00
22	2	1985	0.960	32.01	1366.30	0.75	0.50	1.00	1.00
23	2	1986	0.940	28.81	1229.67	0.75	0.50	1.00	1.00
24	2	1987	0.790	28.81	1229.67	0.75	0.50	1.00	1.00
25	2	1988	0.790	32.29	1378.35	0.75	0.50	1.00	1.00
26	2	1989	0.790	32.82	1400.95	0.75	0.50	1.00	1.00
27	2	1990	0.790	34.75	1483.35	0.75	0.50	1.00	1.00
28	2	1991	0.790	36.70	1566.44	0.75	0.50	1.00	1.00
29	2	1992	0.790	39.89	1702.72	0.75	0.50	1.00	1.00
30	2	1993	0.790	42.61	1818.60	0.75	0.50	1.00	1.00
31	2	1994	0.790	46.02	1964.39	0.75	0.50	1.00	1.00
32	2	1995	0.790	49.73	2122.57	0.75	0.50	1.00	1.00
33	2	1996	0.770	51.49	2197.67	0.75	0.50	1.00	1.00
34	2	1997	0.750	53.85	2298.26	0.75	0.50	1.00	1.00
35	2	1998	0.730	55.83	2382.74	0.75	0.50	1.00	1.00
36	2	1999	0.710	57.91	2471.74	0.75	0.50	1.00	1.00
37	2	2000	0.690	60.11	2565.72	0.75	0.50	1.00	1.00
38	2	2001	0.670	62.98	2688.22	0.75	0.50	1.00	1.00
39	2	2002	0.650	65.44	2793.21	0.75	0.50	1.00	1.00
40	2	2003	0.630	67.82	2894.49	0.75	0.50	1.00	1.00
41	2	2004	0.610	70.57	3011.89	0.75	0.50	1.00	1.00
42	2	2005	0.590	72.90	3111.66	0.75	0.50	1.00	1.00
43	3	1985	0.670	23.46	1667.50	0.50	0.50	1.20	1.00
44	3	1986	0.590	21.11	1500.75	0.50	0.50	1.20	1.00
45	3	1987	0.590	21.11	1500.75	0.50	0.50	1.20	1.00
46	3	1988	0.590	23.12	1643.41	0.50	0.50	1.20	1.00
47	3	1989	0.590	23.62	1679.42	0.50	0.50	1.20	1.00
48	3	1990	0.590	24.87	1768.01	0.50	0.50	1.20	1.00
49	3	1991	0.590	26.09	1854.97	0.50	0.50	1.20	1.00
50	3	1992	0.590	28.19	2003.87	0.50	0.50	1.20	1.00
51	3	1993	0.590	29.91	2126.09	0.50	0.50	1.20	1.00
52	3	1994	0.590	32.12	2283.71	0.50	0.50	1.20	1.00
53	3	1995	0.590	34.51	2453.65	0.50	0.50	1.20	1.00
54	3	1996	0.570	35.75	2541.49	0.50	0.50	1.20	1.00
55	3	1997	0.550	37.38	2657.49	0.50	0.50	1.20	1.00
56	3	1998	0.530	38.75	2754.68	0.50	0.50	1.20	1.00
57	3	1999	0.510	40.20	2858.09	0.50	0.50	1.20	1.00
58	3	2000	0.490	41.73	2966.99	0.50	0.50	1.20	1.00
59	3	2001	0.470	43.71	3107.28	0.50	0.50	1.20	1.00
60	3	2002	0.450	45.43	3229.51	0.50	0.50	1.20	1.00
61	3	2003	0.430	47.24	3358.09	0.50	0.50	1.20	1.00

Continued on Next Page

(TABLE E.2b continued)

62	3	2004	0.410	49.14	3493.65	0.50	0.50	1.20	1.00
63	3	2005	0.390	50.78	3610.40	0.50	0.50	1.20	1.00
64	4	1985	0.800	30.75	2217.90	1.00	0.50	1.20	1.00
65	4	1986	0.765	27.68	1996.11	1.00	0.50	1.20	1.00
66	4	1987	0.710	27.68	1996.11	1.00	0.50	1.20	1.00
67	4	1988	0.710	29.93	2158.04	1.00	0.50	1.20	1.00
68	4	1989	0.710	31.50	2271.28	1.00	0.50	1.20	1.00
69	4	1990	0.710	33.59	2422.51	1.00	0.50	1.20	1.00
70	4	1991	0.710	36.00	2596.08	1.00	0.50	1.20	1.00
71	4	1992	0.710	39.12	2821.45	1.00	0.50	1.20	1.00
72	4	1993	0.710	41.79	3013.63	1.00	0.50	1.20	1.00
73	4	1994	0.710	45.09	3251.73	1.00	0.50	1.20	1.00
74	4	1995	0.710	48.61	3505.33	1.00	0.50	1.20	1.00
75	4	1996	0.690	50.33	3629.26	1.00	0.50	1.20	1.00
76	4	1997	0.670	52.63	3795.08	1.00	0.50	1.20	1.00
77	4	1998	0.650	54.56	3934.67	1.00	0.50	1.20	1.00
78	4	1999	0.630	56.61	4082.03	1.00	0.50	1.20	1.00
79	4	2000	0.610	58.77	4238.07	1.00	0.50	1.20	1.00
80	4	2001	0.590	61.56	4439.09	1.00	0.50	1.20	1.00
81	4	2002	0.570	63.96	4612.66	1.00	0.50	1.20	1.00
82	4	2003	0.550	66.52	4797.09	1.00	0.50	1.20	1.00
83	4	2004	0.530	69.20	4990.20	1.00	0.50	1.20	1.00
84	4	2005	0.510	71.50	5156.17	1.00	0.50	1.20	1.00
85	5	1985	0.960	28.74	1017.20	0.50	0.50	0.40	1.00
86	5	1986	0.940	25.87	915.48	0.50	0.50	0.40	1.00
87	5	1987	0.940	25.87	915.48	0.50	0.50	0.40	1.00
88	5	1988	0.940	27.56	975.13	0.50	0.50	0.40	1.00
89	5	1989	0.940	28.81	1019.34	0.50	0.50	0.40	1.00
90	5	1990	0.940	30.56	1081.40	0.50	0.50	0.40	1.00
91	5	1991	0.940	32.52	1150.98	0.50	0.50	0.40	1.00
92	5	1992	0.940	35.15	1243.71	0.50	0.50	0.40	1.00
93	5	1993	0.940	37.34	1321.32	0.50	0.50	0.40	1.00
94	5	1994	0.940	40.08	1418.35	0.50	0.50	0.40	1.00
95	5	1995	0.940	43.04	1522.97	0.50	0.50	0.40	1.00
96	5	1996	0.920	44.57	1577.12	3.50	0.50	0.40	1.00
97	5	1997	0.900	46.60	1649.10	0.50	0.50	0.40	1.00
98	5	1998	0.880	48.30	1709.20	0.50	0.50	0.40	1.00
99	5	1999	0.860	50.12	1773.65	0.50	0.50	0.40	1.00
100	5	2000	0.840	52.03	1841.27	0.50	0.50	0.40	1.00
101	5	2001	0.820	54.49	1928.43	0.50	0.50	0.40	1.00
102	5	2002	0.800	56.63	2004.02	0.50	0.50	0.40	1.00
103	5	2003	0.780	58.89	2083.98	0.50	0.50	0.40	1.00
104	5	2004	0.760	61.26	2167.92	0.50	0.50	0.40	1.00
105	5	2005	0.740	63.31	2240.34	0.50	0.50	0.40	1.00
106	6	1985	0.800	33.08	1912.50	0.50	0.50	1.75	1.00
107	6	1986	0.710	29.77	1721.25	0.50	0.50	1.40	1.00
108	6	1987	0.710	29.77	1721.25	0.50	0.50	1.40	1.00
109	6	1988	0.710	31.95	1847.26	0.50	0.50	1.40	1.00
110	6	1989	0.710	33.34	1927.79	0.50	0.50	1.40	1.00
111	6	1990	0.710	35.41	2047.53	0.50	0.50	1.40	1.00
112	6	1991	0.710	37.75	2182.88	0.50	0.50	1.40	1.00
113	6	1992	0.710	40.87	2363.11	0.50	0.50	1.40	1.00
114	6	1993	0.710	43.49	2514.69	0.50	0.50	1.40	1.00
115	6	1994	0.710	46.74	2702.54	0.50	0.50	1.40	1.00
116	6	1995	0.710	50.26	2905.88	0.50	0.50	1.40	1.00
117	6	1996	0.690	52.04	3008.78	0.50	0.50	1.40	1.00
118	6	1997	0.670	54.41	3145.61	0.50	0.50	1.40	1.00
119	6	1998	0.650	56.41	3261.54	0.50	0.50	1.40	1.00
120	6	1999	0.630	58.52	3383.74	0.50	0.50	1.40	1.00
121	6	2000	0.610	60.76	3512.94	0.50	0.50	1.40	1.00
122	6	2001	0.590	63.63	3679.15	0.50	0.50	1.40	1.00
123	6	2002	0.570	66.13	3823.73	0.50	0.50	1.40	1.00
124	6	2003	0.550	68.77	3976.05	0.50	0.50	1.40	1.00
125	6	2004	0.530	71.55	4136.97	0.50	0.50	1.40	1.00
126	6	2005	0.510	73.93	4274.54	0.50	0.50	1.40	1.00

TABLE E.2c

RESULTS

Record#	AREA	YEAR	WELLS	EWELLS	SEWELLS	DWELLS	SDWELLS	EORWELL
1	1	1985	0	0	0	0	0	0.0
2	1	1986	98	14	0	84	61	6.7
3	1	1987	115	16	1	99	72	8.0
4	1	1988	108	15	1	93	67	7.5
5	1	1989	109	15	0	94	68	7.6
6	1	1990	111	16	1	95	69	7.6
7	1	1991	110	16	1	94	68	7.6
8	1	1992	118	17	1	101	73	8.1
9	1	1993	121	17	1	104	75	8.4
10	1	1994	125	18	1	107	77	8.6
11	1	1995	129	18	1	111	80	8.9
12	1	1996	121	17	0	104	75	8.4
13	1	1997	105	15	1	90	65	7.2
14	1	1998	89	13	1	76	55	6.1
15	1	1999	76	11	0	65	47	5.2
16	1	2000	64	9	1	55	40	4.4
17	1	2001	54	8	0	46	33	3.7
18	1	2002	45	6	1	39	28	3.1
19	1	2003	37	5	0	32	23	2.6
20	1	2004	31	4	0	27	20	2.2
21	1	2005	25	4	0	21	15	1.7
22	2	1985	0	0	0	0	0	0.0
23	2	1986	30	3	0	27	21	0.0
24	2	1987	45	5	1	40	31	0.0
25	2	1988	42	5	0	37	28	0.0
26	2	1989	43	5	0	38	29	0.0
27	2	1990	46	5	0	41	32	0.0
28	2	1991	50	6	1	44	34	0.0
29	2	1992	56	6	0	50	38	0.0
30	2	1993	61	7	0	54	42	0.0
31	2	1994	67	7	1	60	46	0.0
32	2	1995	74	8	0	66	51	0.0
33	2	1996	76	8	0	68	52	0.0
34	2	1997	76	8	1	68	52	0.0
35	2	1998	75	8	0	67	52	0.0
36	2	1999	73	8	1	65	50	0.0
37	2	2000	72	8	0	64	49	0.0
38	2	2001	71	8	0	63	48	0.0
39	2	2002	70	8	1	62	48	0.0
40	2	2003	67	7	0	60	46	0.0
41	2	2004	66	7	1	59	45	0.0
42	2	2005	63	7	0	56	43	0.0
43	3	1985	0	0	0	0	0	0.0
44	3	1986	27	3	0	24	14	1.6
45	3	1987	30	3	0	27	16	1.8
46	3	1988	38	4	0	34	21	2.3
47	3	1989	42	5	1	37	22	2.5
48	3	1990	43	5	0	38	23	2.5
49	3	1991	45	5	0	40	24	2.7
50	3	1992	47	5	0	42	25	2.8
51	3	1993	49	6	1	43	26	2.9
52	3	1994	52	6	0	46	28	3.1
53	3	1995	55	6	0	49	30	3.3
54	3	1996	57	7	1	50	30	3.3
55	3	1997	60	7	0	53	32	3.6
56	3	1998	63	7	0	56	34	3.8
57	3	1999	66	8	1	58	35	3.9
58	3	2000	69	8	0	61	37	4.1
59	3	2001	72	8	1	64	39	4.3
60	3	2002	76	9	0	67	40	4.5
61	3	2003	79	9	0	70	42	4.7

Continued on Next Page

(TABLE E.2c continued)

62	3	2004	83	10	1	73	44	4.9
63	3	2005	87	10	0	77	46	5.2
64	4	1985	0	0	0	0	0	0.0
65	4	1986	113	15	1	98	74	0.0
66	4	1987	140	18	1	122	92	0.0
67	4	1988	148	19	1	129	97	0.0
68	4	1989	152	20	1	132	99	0.0
69	4	1990	158	21	1	137	103	0.0
70	4	1991	165	21	1	144	108	0.0
71	4	1992	174	23	1	151	113	0.0
72	4	1993	182	24	2	158	119	0.0
73	4	1994	191	25	1	166	125	0.0
74	4	1995	200	26	1	174	131	0.0
75	4	1996	204	27	1	177	133	0.0
76	4	1997	211	27	2	184	138	0.0
77	4	1998	216	28	1	188	141	0.0
78	4	1999	222	29	2	193	145	0.0
79	4	2000	228	30	1	198	149	0.0
80	4	2001	235	31	2	204	153	0.0
81	4	2002	242	31	1	211	158	0.0
82	4	2003	248	32	2	216	162	0.0
83	4	2004	255	33	1	222	167	0.0
84	4	2005	261	34	2	227	170	0.0
85	5	1985	0	0	0	0	0	0.0
86	5	1986	114	13	1	101	78	0.0
87	5	1987	111	12	0	99	76	0.0
88	5	1988	120	13	1	107	82	0.0
89	5	1989	125	14	1	111	85	0.0
90	5	1990	130	14	0	116	89	0.0
91	5	1991	137	15	1	122	94	0.0
92	5	1992	145	16	1	129	99	0.0
93	5	1993	153	17	1	136	105	0.0
94	5	1994	161	18	1	143	110	0.0
95	5	1995	171	19	1	152	117	0.0
96	5	1996	176	20	1	156	120	0.0
97	5	1997	179	20	1	159	122	0.0
98	5	1998	182	20	1	162	125	0.0
99	5	1999	185	21	1	164	126	0.0
100	5	2000	188	21	1	167	128	0.0
101	5	2001	191	21	1	170	131	0.0
102	5	2002	195	22	1	173	133	0.0
103	5	2003	197	22	1	175	135	0.0
104	5	2004	200	22	1	178	137	0.0
105	5	2005	203	23	1	180	138	0.0
106	6	1985	0	0	0	0	0	0.0
107	6	1986	146	12	1	134	101	0.0
108	6	1987	162	14	1	148	111	0.0
109	6	1988	174	15	0	159	119	0.0
110	6	1989	180	15	1	165	124	0.0
111	6	1990	186	16	1	170	128	0.0
112	6	1991	194	16	1	178	134	0.0
113	6	1992	203	17	1	186	140	0.0
114	6	1993	212	18	0	194	146	0.0
115	6	1994	222	19	1	203	152	0.0
116	6	1995	232	20	1	212	159	0.0
117	6	1996	240	20	1	220	165	0.0
118	6	1997	247	21	1	226	170	0.0
119	6	1998	254	22	2	232	174	0.0
120	6	1999	260	22	1	238	179	0.0
121	6	2000	267	23	1	244	183	0.0
122	6	2001	275	23	1	252	189	0.0
123	6	2002	283	24	1	259	195	0.0
124	6	2003	291	25	1	266	200	0.0
125	6	2004	299	25	2	274	206	0.0
126	6	2005	307	26	1	281	211	0.0

E.3

HIGH CASE TABLES

TABLE E.3a

PRICE INPUT

Record#	AREA	YEAR	PROFIT	POIL	PGAS	ROYOIL	ROYGAS
1	1	1985	133.24	198.44	133.59	0.1600	0.1480
2	1	1986	33.98	87.09	138.46	0.1600	0.1570
3	1	1987	41.01	105.10	129.66	0.0470	0.2300
4	1	1988	63.64	163.10	79.31	0.0470	0.2300
5	1	1989	66.38	170.14	84.67	0.0530	0.2300
6	1	1990	69.97	179.32	92.30	0.0590	0.2300
7	1	1991	70.14	179.76	103.35	0.0670	0.2300
8	1	1992	78.19	200.39	112.51	0.0750	0.2300
9	1	1993	83.12	213.04	122.03	0.0830	0.2300
10	1	1994	88.55	226.94	136.18	0.0920	0.2030
11	1	1995	94.39	241.84	142.24	0.1020	0.2300
12	1	1996	100.03	256.37	192.11	0.1020	0.0000
13	1	1997	106.02	271.72	199.79	0.1020	0.0000
14	1	1998	112.37	288.01	207.80	0.1020	0.0000
15	1	1999	119.12	305.31	216.12	0.1020	0.0000
16	1	2000	126.29	323.67	224.74	0.1020	0.0000
17	1	2001	133.85	343.05	233.74	0.1020	0.0000
18	1	2002	141.87	363.61	243.08	0.1020	0.0000
19	1	2003	150.39	385.44	252.81	0.1020	0.0000
20	1	2004	159.42	408.59	262.93	0.1020	0.0000
21	1	2005	168.99	433.12	273.45	0.1020	0.0000
22	2	1985	204.17	199.58	0.00	0.2100	0.1480
23	2	1986	30.15	89.67	138.46	0.2200	0.1570
24	2	1987	35.61	105.92	129.66	0.1070	0.2300
25	2	1988	55.66	165.55	79.31	0.1070	0.2300
26	2	1989	57.50	171.02	84.67	0.1130	0.2300
27	2	1990	60.59	180.20	92.30	0.1190	0.2300
28	2	1991	63.70	189.45	103.35	0.1270	0.2300
29	2	1992	67.67	201.27	112.51	0.1350	0.2300
30	2	1993	71.93	213.92	122.03	0.1430	0.2300
31	2	1994	76.60	227.82	131.56	0.1520	0.2300
32	2	1995	81.59	242.66	142.24	0.1620	0.2300
33	2	1996	86.50	257.25	192.11	0.1620	0.0000
34	2	1997	91.68	272.66	199.79	0.1620	0.0000
35	2	1998	97.18	289.02	207.80	0.1620	0.0000
36	2	1999	103.02	306.38	216.12	0.1620	0.0000
37	2	2000	109.19	324.74	224.74	0.1620	0.0000
38	2	2001	115.74	344.24	233.74	0.1620	0.0000
39	2	2002	122.68	364.87	243.08	0.1620	0.0000
40	2	2003	130.06	386.82	252.81	0.1620	0.0000
41	2	2004	137.87	410.03	262.93	0.1620	0.0000
42	2	2005	146.14	434.63	273.45	0.1620	0.0000
43	3	1985	63.57	187.06	133.59	0.3000	0.1480
44	3	1986	33.98	100.56	138.46	0.3100	0.1570
45	3	1987	40.70	120.20	129.66	0.2190	0.2300
46	3	1988	44.57	183.54	79.31	0.2190	0.2300
47	3	1989	45.55	183.54	84.67	0.2250	0.2300
48	3	1990	47.95	199.76	92.30	0.2310	0.2300
49	3	1991	50.31	208.70	103.35	0.2380	0.2300
50	3	1992	54.35	220.21	112.51	0.2450	0.2300
51	3	1993	57.66	232.60	122.03	0.2530	0.2300
52	3	1994	61.95	246.31	131.56	0.2610	0.2300
53	3	1995	66.54	260.96	142.24	0.2690	0.2300
54	3	1996	68.93	276.63	192.11	0.2690	0.0000
55	3	1997	72.07	293.23	199.79	0.2690	0.0000
56	3	1998	74.71	310.84	207.80	0.2690	0.0000
57	3	1999	77.51	329.46	216.12	0.2690	0.0000
58	3	2000	80.47	349.27	224.74	0.2690	0.0000
59	3	2001	84.27	370.22	233.74	0.2690	0.0000
60	3	2002	87.59	392.42	243.08	0.2690	0.0000
61	3	2003	91.07	415.95	252.81	0.2690	0.0000
62	3	2004	94.74	440.92	262.93	0.2690	0.0000

Continued on Next Page

(TABLE E.3a continued)

63	3	2005	97.92	467.40	273.45	0.2690	0.0000
64	4	1985	78.86	207.82	133.59	0.2500	0.1480
65	4	1986	85.32	107.61	138.46	0.2600	0.1570
66	4	1987	101.88	128.50	129.66	0.2010	0.2300
67	4	1988	153.50	193.60	79.31	0.2010	0.2300
68	4	1989	164.17	207.06	84.67	0.2070	0.2300
69	4	1990	174.34	219.89	92.30	0.2130	0.2300
70	4	1991	185.97	234.55	103.35	0.2190	0.2300
71	4	1992	197.49	249.08	112.51	0.2260	0.2300
72	4	1993	209.95	264.80	122.03	0.2320	0.2300
73	4	1994	223.37	281.72	131.56	0.2390	0.2300
74	4	1995	237.43	299.46	142.24	0.2460	0.2300
75	4	1996	251.64	317.38	192.11	0.2460	0.0000
76	4	1997	266.75	336.44	199.79	0.2460	0.0000
77	4	1998	282.76	356.63	207.80	0.2460	0.0000
78	4	1999	299.72	378.02	216.12	0.2460	0.0000
79	4	2000	317.72	400.72	224.74	0.2460	0.0000
80	4	2001	336.77	424.75	233.74	0.2460	0.0000
81	4	2002	356.97	450.23	243.08	0.2460	0.0000
82	4	2003	378.41	477.27	252.81	0.2460	0.0000
83	4	2004	401.10	505.89	262.93	0.2460	0.0000
84	4	2005	425.19	536.27	273.45	0.2460	0.0000
85	5	1985	204.17	241.16	133.59	0.0800	0.1480
86	5	1986	30.15	121.64	138.46	0.0800	0.1570
87	5	1987	35.81	144.48	129.66	0.0180	0.2300
88	5	1988	53.19	214.61	79.31	0.0180	0.2300
89	5	1989	56.52	228.01	84.67	0.0185	0.2300
90	5	1990	59.66	240.71	92.30	0.0188	0.2300
91	5	1991	63.22	255.05	103.35	0.0191	0.2300
92	5	1992	66.72	269.20	112.51	0.0194	0.2300
93	5	1993	70.58	284.74	122.03	0.0197	0.2300
94	5	1994	74.71	301.41	131.56	0.0200	0.2300
95	5	1995	79.07	319.02	142.24	0.0203	0.2300
96	5	1996	83.81	338.14	192.11	0.0203	0.0000
97	5	1997	88.85	358.46	199.79	0.0203	0.0000
98	5	1998	94.18	379.97	207.80	0.0203	0.0000
99	5	1999	99.82	402.74	216.12	0.0203	0.0000
100	5	2000	105.81	426.89	224.74	0.0203	0.0000
101	5	2001	112.16	452.49	233.74	0.0203	0.0000
102	5	2002	118.89	479.66	243.08	0.0203	0.0000
103	5	2003	126.03	508.47	252.81	0.0203	0.0000
104	5	2004	133.59	538.97	262.93	0.0203	0.0000
105	5	2005	141.60	571.30	273.45	0.0203	0.0000
106	6	1985	140.81	210.97	133.59	0.2500	0.1480
107	6	1986	78.66	117.80	138.46	0.2600	0.1570
108	6	1987	93.56	139.76	132.19	0.1760	0.2300
109	6	1988	139.96	209.07	79.31	0.1760	0.2300
110	6	1989	148.47	221.78	84.67	0.1800	0.2300
111	6	1990	157.02	234.55	92.30	0.1850	0.2300
112	6	1991	166.62	248.89	103.35	0.1890	0.2300
113	6	1992	176.22	263.23	112.51	0.1930	0.2300
114	6	1993	186.66	278.83	122.03	0.1980	0.2300
115	6	1994	197.82	295.50	131.56	0.2020	0.2300
116	6	1995	209.65	313.17	142.24	0.2070	0.2300
117	6	1996	222.19	331.91	192.11	0.2070	0.0000
118	6	1997	235.54	351.85	199.79	0.2070	0.0000
119	6	1998	249.69	372.99	207.80	0.2070	0.0000
120	6	1999	264.81	395.57	216.12	0.2070	0.0000
121	6	2000	280.56	419.09	224.74	0.2070	0.0000
122	6	2001	297.36	444.19	233.74	0.2070	0.0000
123	6	2002	315.21	470.86	243.08	0.2070	0.0000
124	6	2003	334.12	499.10	252.81	0.2070	0.0000
125	6	2004	354.16	529.10	262.93	0.2070	0.0000
126	6	2005	375.42	560.80	1675.86	0.2070	0.0000

TABLE E.3b

COST INPUT

Record#	AREA	YEAR	SUCCESS	OPCOST	DRILLCOST	EWEIGHT	SWEIGHT	DUP	DUF
1	1	1985	0.820	38.80	1253.00	1.00	0.50	1.00	1.00
2	1	1986	0.750	34.92	1127.70	1.00	0.50	1.00	1.00
3	1	1987	0.720	34.92	1127.70	1.00	0.50	1.00	1.00
4	1	1988	0.720	54.19	1750.03	1.00	0.50	1.00	1.00
5	1	1989	0.720	56.53	1825.56	1.00	0.50	1.00	1.00
6	1	1990	0.720	59.58	1924.06	1.00	0.50	1.00	1.00
7	1	1991	0.720	59.73	1928.79	1.00	0.50	1.00	1.00
8	1	1992	0.720	66.58	2150.14	1.00	0.50	1.00	1.00
9	1	1993	0.720	70.78	2285.87	1.00	0.50	1.00	1.00
10	1	1994	0.720	75.40	2435.02	1.00	0.50	1.00	1.00
11	1	1995	0.720	80.35	2594.89	1.00	0.50	1.00	1.00
12	1	1996	0.700	85.18	2750.79	1.00	0.50	1.00	1.00
13	1	1997	0.680	90.28	2915.50	1.00	0.50	1.00	1.00
14	1	1998	0.660	95.69	3090.28	1.00	0.50	1.00	1.00
15	1	1999	0.640	101.44	3275.91	1.00	0.50	1.00	1.00
16	1	2000	0.620	107.54	3472.91	1.00	0.50	1.00	1.00
17	1	2001	0.600	113.98	3680.85	1.00	0.50	1.00	1.00
18	1	2002	0.580	120.81	3901.46	1.00	0.50	1.00	1.00
19	1	2003	0.560	128.06	4135.69	1.00	0.50	1.00	1.00
20	1	2004	0.540	135.76	4384.08	1.00	0.50	1.00	1.00
21	1	2005	0.520	143.91	4647.28	1.00	0.50	1.00	1.00
22	2	1985	0.960	32.01	1366.31	0.75	0.50	1.00	1.00
23	2	1986	0.940	28.81	1229.67	0.75	0.50	1.00	1.00
24	2	1987	0.790	28.81	1229.67	0.75	0.50	1.00	1.00
25	2	1988	0.790	45.03	1921.94	0.75	0.50	1.00	1.00
26	2	1989	0.790	46.52	1985.44	0.75	0.50	1.00	1.00
27	2	1990	0.790	49.01	2092.02	0.75	0.50	1.00	1.00
28	2	1991	0.790	51.53	2199.41	0.75	0.50	1.00	1.00
29	2	1992	0.790	54.74	2336.63	0.75	0.50	1.00	1.00
30	2	1993	0.799	58.19	2483.49	0.75	0.50	1.00	1.00
31	2	1994	0.790	61.97	2644.86	0.75	0.50	1.00	1.00
32	2	1995	0.790	66.00	2817.14	0.75	0.50	1.00	1.00
33	2	1996	0.770	69.94	2986.52	0.75	0.50	1.00	1.00
34	2	1997	0.750	74.16	3165.43	0.75	0.50	1.00	1.00
35	2	1998	0.730	78.61	3355.36	0.75	0.50	1.00	1.00
36	2	1999	0.710	83.33	3556.89	0.75	0.50	1.00	1.00
37	2	2000	0.690	88.33	3770.04	0.75	0.50	1.00	1.00
38	2	2001	0.670	93.63	3996.43	0.75	0.50	1.00	1.00
39	2	2002	0.650	99.24	4235.93	0.75	0.50	1.00	1.00
40	2	2003	0.630	105.21	4490.76	0.75	0.50	1.00	1.00
41	2	2004	0.610	111.53	4760.21	0.75	0.50	1.00	1.00
42	2	2005	0.590	118.22	5045.80	0.75	0.50	1.00	1.00
43	3	1985	0.670	23.46	1667.50	0.50	0.50	1.20	1.00
44	3	1986	0.590	21.11	1500.75	0.50	0.50	1.20	1.00
45	3	1987	0.590	21.11	1500.75	0.50	0.50	1.20	1.00
46	3	1988	0.590	32.23	2291.58	0.50	0.50	1.20	1.00
47	3	1989	0.590	33.49	2381.10	0.50	0.50	1.20	1.00
48	3	1990	0.590	35.08	2494.09	0.50	0.50	1.20	1.00
49	3	1991	0.590	36.65	2605.71	0.50	0.50	1.20	1.00
50	3	1992	0.590	38.67	2749.42	0.50	0.50	1.20	1.00
51	3	1993	0.590	40.85	2904.11	0.50	0.50	1.20	1.00
52	3	1994	0.590	43.26	3075.29	0.50	0.50	1.20	1.00
53	3	1995	0.590	45.83	3258.20	0.50	0.50	1.20	1.00
54	3	1996	0.570	48.58	3453.85	0.50	0.50	1.20	1.00
55	3	1997	0.550	51.50	3661.11	0.50	0.50	1.20	1.00
56	3	1998	0.530	54.59	3880.97	0.50	0.50	1.20	1.00
57	3	1999	0.510	57.86	4113.45	0.50	0.50	1.20	1.00
58	3	2000	0.490	61.34	4360.79	0.50	0.50	1.20	1.00
59	3	2001	0.470	65.02	4622.36	0.50	0.50	1.20	1.00
60	3	2002	0.450	68.92	4899.54	0.50	0.50	1.20	1.00
61	3	2003	0.430	73.05	5193.32	0.50	0.50	1.20	1.00
62	3	2004	0.410	77.44	5505.08	0.50	0.50	1.20	1.00

Continued on Next Page

(TABLE E.3b continued)

63	3	2005	0.390	82.09	5835.70	0.50	0.50	1.20	1.00
64	4	1985	0.800	30.75	2217.90	1.00	0.50	1.20	1.00
65	4	1986	0.765	27.68	1996.11	1.00	0.50	1.20	1.00
66	4	1987	0.710	27.68	1996.11	1.00	0.50	1.20	1.00
67	4	1988	0.710	41.70	3007.37	1.00	0.50	1.20	1.00
68	4	1989	0.710	44.60	3216.46	1.00	0.50	1.20	1.00
69	4	1990	0.710	47.37	3415.76	1.00	0.50	1.20	1.00
70	4	1991	0.710	50.52	3643.48	1.00	0.50	1.20	1.00
71	4	1992	0.710	53.65	3869.19	1.00	0.50	1.20	1.00
72	4	1993	0.710	57.04	4113.38	1.00	0.50	1.20	1.00
73	4	1994	0.710	60.68	4376.22	1.00	0.50	1.20	1.00
74	4	1995	0.710	64.51	4651.79	1.00	0.50	1.20	1.00
75	4	1996	0.690	68.37	4930.16	1.00	0.50	1.20	1.00
76	4	1997	0.670	72.47	5226.24	1.00	0.50	1.20	1.00
77	4	1998	0.650	76.82	5539.87	1.00	0.50	1.20	1.00
78	4	1999	0.630	81.43	5872.14	1.00	0.50	1.20	1.00
79	4	2000	0.610	86.32	6224.76	1.00	0.50	1.20	1.00
80	4	2001	0.590	91.49	6598.04	1.00	0.50	1.20	1.00
81	4	2002	0.570	96.98	6993.84	1.00	0.50	1.20	1.00
82	4	2003	0.550	102.81	7413.88	1.00	0.50	1.20	1.00
83	4	2004	0.530	108.97	7858.46	1.00	0.50	1.20	1.00
84	4	2005	0.510	115.52	8330.38	1.00	0.50	1.20	1.00
85	5	1985	0.960	28.74	1017.20	0.50	0.50	0.40	1.00
86	5	1986	0.940	25.87	915.48	0.50	0.50	0.40	1.00
87	5	1987	0.940	25.87	915.48	0.50	0.50	0.40	1.00
88	5	1988	0.940	38.43	1359.85	0.50	0.50	0.40	1.00
89	5	1989	0.940	40.83	1444.76	0.50	0.50	0.40	1.00
90	5	1990	0.940	43.10	1525.23	0.50	0.50	0.40	1.00
91	5	1991	0.940	45.67	1616.09	0.50	0.50	0.40	1.00
92	5	1992	0.940	48.20	1705.75	0.50	0.50	0.40	1.00
93	5	1993	0.940	50.98	1804.22	0.50	0.50	0.40	1.00
94	5	1994	0.940	53.97	1909.85	0.50	0.50	0.40	1.00
95	5	1995	0.940	57.12	2021.43	0.50	0.50	0.40	1.00
96	5	1996	0.920	60.55	2142.58	0.50	0.50	0.40	1.00
97	5	1997	0.900	64.18	2271.34	0.50	0.50	0.40	1.00
98	5	1998	0.880	68.04	2407.63	0.50	0.50	0.40	1.00
99	5	1999	0.860	72.11	2551.91	0.50	0.50	0.40	1.00
100	5	2000	0.840	76.44	2704.94	0.50	0.50	0.40	1.00
101	5	2001	0.820	81.02	2867.15	0.50	0.50	0.40	1.00
102	5	2002	0.800	85.89	3039.31	0.50	0.50	0.40	1.00
103	5	2003	0.780	91.04	3221.46	0.50	0.50	0.40	1.00
104	5	2004	0.760	96.51	3415.12	0.50	0.50	0.40	1.00
105	5	2005	0.740	102.29	1619.97	0.50	0.50	0.40	1.00
106	6	1985	0.800	33.08	1912.50	0.50	0.50	1.40	1.00
107	6	1986	0.710	29.77	1721.50	0.50	0.50	1.40	1.00
108	6	1987	0.710	29.77	1721.50	0.50	0.50	1.40	1.00
109	6	1988	0.710	44.53	2561.77	0.50	0.50	1.40	1.00
110	6	1989	0.710	47.24	2717.50	0.50	0.50	1.40	1.00
111	6	1990	0.710	49.96	2873.98	0.50	0.50	1.40	1.00
112	6	1991	0.710	53.02	3049.69	0.50	0.50	1.40	1.00
113	6	1992	0.710	56.07	3225.40	0.50	0.50	1.40	1.00
114	6	1993	0.710	59.39	3416.55	0.50	0.50	1.40	1.00
115	6	1994	0.710	62.94	3620.81	0.50	0.50	1.40	1.00
116	6	1995	0.710	66.71	3837.32	0.50	0.50	1.40	1.00
117	6	1996	0.690	70.70	4066.94	0.50	0.50	1.40	1.00
118	6	1997	0.670	74.95	4311.27	0.50	0.50	1.40	1.00
119	6	1998	0.650	79.45	4570.30	0.50	0.50	1.40	1.00
120	6	1999	0.630	84.26	4846.98	0.50	0.50	1.40	1.00
121	6	2000	0.610	89.27	5135.17	0.50	0.50	1.40	1.00
122	6	2001	0.590	94.62	5442.73	0.50	0.50	1.40	1.00
123	6	2002	0.570	100.30	5769.52	0.50	0.50	1.40	1.00
124	6	2003	0.550	106.31	6115.55	0.50	0.50	1.40	1.00
125	6	2004	0.530	112.69	6482.41	0.50	0.50	1.40	1.00
126	6	2005	0.510	119.45	6871.57	0.50	0.50	1.40	1.00

TABLE E.3c

RESULTS

Record#	AREA	YEAR	WELLS	EWELLS	SEWELLS	DWELLS	SDWELLS	EORWELL
1	1	1985	0	0	0	0	0	0
2	1	1986	98	14	0	84	61	7
3	1	1987	114	16	1	98	71	8
4	1	1988	132	19	1	113	82	9
5	1	1989	134	19	1	115	83	9
6	1	1990	137	19	1	118	85	9
7	1	1991	135	19	1	116	84	9
8	1	1992	143	20	1	123	89	10
9	1	1993	146	21	1	125	90	10
10	1	1994	150	21	1	129	93	10
11	1	1995	153	22	1	131	95	11
12	1	1996	145	20	1	125	90	10
13	1	1997	126	18	1	108	78	9
14	1	1998	109	15	1	94	68	8
15	1	1999	94	13	0	81	59	7
16	1	2000	81	11	1	70	51	6
17	1	2001	69	10	0	59	43	5
18	1	2002	58	8	1	50	36	4
19	1	2003	49	7	0	42	30	3
20	1	2004	40	6	0	34	25	3
21	1	2005	33	5	1	28	20	2
22	2	1985	0	0	0	0	0	0
23	2	1986	31	3	0	28	22	0
24	2	1987	44	5	0	39	30	0
25	2	1988	70	8	0	62	48	0
26	2	1989	74	8	1	66	51	0
27	2	1990	79	9	0	70	54	0
28	2	1991	84	9	1	75	58	0
29	2	1992	91	10	0	81	62	0
30	2	1993	100	11	1	89	68	0
31	2	1994	108	12	0	96	74	0
32	2	1995	115	13	1	102	78	0
33	2	1996	122	14	1	108	83	0
34	2	1997	125	14	0	111	85	0
35	2	1998	127	14	1	113	87	0
36	2	1999	129	14	1	115	88	0
37	2	2000	131	15	1	116	89	0
38	2	2001	132	15	0	117	90	0
39	2	2002	133	15	1	118	91	0
40	2	2003	134	15	1	119	91	0
41	2	2004	135	15	1	120	92	0
42	2	2005	135	15	0	120	92	0
43	3	1985	0	0	0	0	0	0
44	3	1986	38	4	1	34	21	2
45	3	1987	46	5	0	41	25	3
46	3	1988	69	8	0	61	37	4
47	3	1989	69	8	1	61	37	4
48	3	1990	74	9	0	65	39	4
49	3	1991	76	9	0	67	40	4
50	3	1992	79	9	1	70	42	5
51	3	1993	83	10	0	73	44	5
52	3	1994	87	10	1	77	46	5
53	3	1995	91	11	0	80	48	5
54	3	1996	94	11	1	83	50	6
55	3	1997	99	12	1	87	52	6
56	3	1998	104	12	0	92	55	6
57	3	1999	109	13	1	96	58	6
58	3	2000	115	13	1	102	62	7
59	3	2001	121	14	0	107	65	7
60	3	2002	127	15	1	112	68	8
61	3	2003	134	16	1	118	71	8
62	3	2004	141	16	1	125	75	8

Continued on Next Page

(TABLE E.3c continued)

63	3	2005	148	17	0	131	79	9
64	4	1985	0	0	0	0	0	0
65	4	1986	142	18	1	124	93	0
66	4	1987	175	23	2	152	114	0
67	4	1988	233	30	1	203	152	0
68	4	1989	243	32	2	211	158	0
69	4	1990	252	33	1	219	164	0
70	4	1991	262	34	2	228	171	0
71	4	1992	272	35	2	237	178	0
72	4	1993	282	37	2	245	184	0
73	4	1994	293	38	1	255	192	0
74	4	1995	304	40	2	264	198	0
75	4	1996	317	41	2	276	207	0
76	4	1997	330	43	3	287	216	0
77	4	1998	344	45	2	299	225	0
78	4	1999	358	47	2	311	234	0
79	4	2000	373	48	3	325	244	0
80	4	2001	388	50	2	338	254	0
81	4	2002	404	53	3	351	264	0
82	4	2003	421	55	3	366	275	0
83	4	2004	439	57	2	382	287	0
84	4	2005	457	59	3	398	299	0
85	5	1985	0	0	0	0	0	0
86	5	1986	143	16	1	127	98	0
87	5	1987	105	12	1	93	72	0
88	5	1988	137	15	0	122	94	0
89	5	1989	155	17	1	138	106	0
90	5	1990	162	18	1	144	111	0
91	5	1991	170	19	1	151	116	0
92	5	1992	177	20	1	157	121	0
93	5	1993	185	21	1	164	126	0
94	5	1994	194	22	1	172	132	0
95	5	1995	203	23	1	180	138	0
96	5	1996	211	23	2	188	145	0
97	5	1997	218	24	1	194	149	0
98	5	1998	225	25	1	200	154	0
99	5	1999	232	26	1	206	158	0
100	5	2000	240	27	2	213	164	0
101	5	2001	247	27	1	220	169	0
102	5	2002	255	28	1	227	175	0
103	5	2003	263	29	2	234	180	0
104	5	2004	271	30	1	241	185	0
105	5	2005	279	31	2	248	191	0
106	6	1985	0	0	0	0	0	0
107	6	1986	216	18	1	198	149	0
108	6	1987	239	20	1	219	164	0
109	6	1988	300	25	1	275	207	0
110	6	1989	337	29	2	308	231	0
111	6	1990	349	30	1	319	240	0
112	6	1991	362	31	2	331	249	0
113	6	1992	376	32	1	344	258	0
114	6	1993	389	33	2	356	267	0
115	6	1994	404	34	2	370	278	0
116	6	1995	419	36	1	383	288	0
117	6	1996	436	37	2	399	300	0
118	6	1997	454	39	2	415	312	0
119	6	1998	473	40	2	433	325	0
120	6	1999	493	42	2	451	339	0
121	6	2000	513	44	2	469	352	0
122	6	2001	534	45	3	489	367	0
123	6	2002	556	47	2	509	382	0
124	6	2003	579	49	3	530	398	0
125	6	2004	603	51	2	552	415	0
126	6	2005	628	53	3	575	432	0

CANADIAN ENERGY RESEARCH INSTITUTE PUBLICATIONS

DECEMBER 1987

CANADIAN ENERGY RESEARCH INSTITUTE

PUBLICATIONS SINCE JANUARY 1, 1983

Studies

No. 25   An Evaluation of Crude Oil Supply in Saskatchewan. James
          Tanner. December 1987 (Price $30.00, 156 pages) ISBN
          0-920522-44-0.

No. 24   Industrial Cogeneration in Canada: Prospects and Perspec-
          tives. Anthony E. Reinsch and Ellen F. Battle. March 1987
          (Price $30.00, 137 pages) ISBN 0-920522-41-6.

No. 23   Energy Efficiency in Canada's Pulp & Paper Industry. Ellen F.
          Battle. October 1986 (Price $35.00, 131 pages) ISBN
          0-920522-38-6.

No. 22   Natural Gas for Vehicles in Canada: A Study of Market
          Penetration Problems. Brian D. Sumner. April 1985 (Price
          $20.00, 99 pages) ISBN 0-920522-37-8.

No. 21   Canadian and U.S. Heavy Crude Oil Markets: A Review and
          Prospects. Volume I. Canadian Energy Research Institute.
          April 1985 (Price $25.00, 175 pages) ISBN 0-920522-36-X.

          Appendix Volume to Study No. 21. Canadian and U.S. Heavy
          Crude Oil Markets: A Review and Prospects. Volume II.
          Canadian Energy Research Institute. April 1985 (Price $10.00,
          133 pages).

No. 20   The Oil and Gas Investment Climate: Changes Over a Decade.
          DataMetrics Limited. June 1984 (Price $15.00, 76 pages)
          ISBN 0-920522-31-9.

          Appendix Volume to Study No. 20. The Oil and Gas Investment
          Climate: Changes Over a Decade. DataMetrics Limited. June
          1984 (Price $12.00, 141 pages).

No. 19   Modelling Exploration Success in Alberta Oil Plays. Kenneth
          D. Foat and Alan J. MacFadyen. September 1983 (Price $15.00,
          181 pages) ISBN 0-920522-29-7.

No. 18   Household Energy Savings: Options for the Future.
          Brian D. Sumner and Barbara E. Green. March 1983
          (Price $20.00, 194 pages) ISBN 0-920522-27-0.

No. 17   Energy and Regional Investment in Canada. Gordon W. Douglas
          and Ellen F. Battle. March 1983 (Price $20.00, 114 pages)
          ISBN 0-920522-28-9.

Research Reports

87-2   A Peak Load Forecasting Model Case Study: The Alberta
         Interconnected System. K. Morgan MacRae. July 1987
         (Price $20.00, 81 pages) ISBN 0920522-42-4.

87-1   Oil and Gas Finding Costs in Alberta: 1970 - 1985.
         Janice L. Pasay. January 1987 (Price $20.00, 87 pages)
         ISBN 0-920522-40-8.

86-2   Reserves of Hydrocarbons in Alberta: A Review of Canadian
         Petroleum Association and Alberta Energy Resources
         Conservation Board Estimates and Methodology. James N.
         Tanner. November 1986 (Price $25.00, 130 pages) ISBN
         0-920522-39-4.

86-1   The Effect of the Western Accord and Recent Provincial Royalty
         Changes on Petroleum Industry Capital Expenditures. Janice L.
         Pasay. March 1986 (Price $15.00, 27 pages).

85-2   Estimated Petroleum Finding Costs in Alberta, 1970-1983.
         Z. Charles Slagorsky and Janice L. Pasay. October 1985
         (Price $15.00, 62 pages).

85-1   The Wolf Lake Project: An Example of Benefits to the Canadian
         Economy from Commercial Oil Sands Development. Louise Czaja,
         Michael Kirkegaard, Walter Haessel and Gordon Douglas. March
         1985 (Price $10.00, 67 pages).

84-1   The Costs of Transportation Fuel from Methanol versus Oil
         Sands. Brian D. Sumner, Tricia Gibson, and Z. Charles
         Slagorsky. December 1984 (Price $20.00, 100 pages) ISBN
         0-920522-34-3.

83-1   Potential Benefits and Costs of Canadian Electricity Exports.
         Ellen F. Battle, Gordon S. Gislason, and Gordon W. Douglas.
         April 1983 (Price $25.00, 288 pages) ISBN 0-920522-26-2.

Working Papers

85-2   A Partial Regional Comparison of Taxes and Subsidies on
         Natural Gas, Electricity, and Oil Products in Canada. L. Coad
         and K. Desbarats. May 1985 (Price $10.00, 78 pages).

85-1   The Implications of Canadian Natural Gas Deregulation.
         Douglas J. Haughey and Robert T. Liddle. January 1985 (Price
         $10.00, 97 pages).

84-3   The CERI Energy Pricing and Demand Models: A Description and
        Internal Evaluation. L. A. Coad. October 1984 (Price $10.00,
        45 pages).

84-2   An Assessment of Benefits and Costs of Using Methanol as a
        Motor Gasoline Extender in Southern Ontario. Walter Haessel
        and Tricia Gibson. September 1984 (Price $10.00, 62 pages).

84-1   A Review of Oil and Gas Drilling Activity Forecasting
        Techniques. G. E. Angevine, S. R. Cain, and Z. C. Slagorsky.
        March 1984 (Price $5.00, 20 pages).

83-6   The Potential for Energy Substitution in Canada.
        Brian D. Sumner. September 1983 (Price $7.50, 124 pages).

83-4   The Impacts of Crude Oil Supply Changes and Supply Allocation.
        Douglas J. Haughey and Donald A. Bruton. May 1983
        (Price $7.50, 72 pages).

83-3   Development Options for British Columbia Coal. Kristi E.
        Varangu. April 1983 (Price $7.50, 107 pages).

83-2   Development Options for Alberta and Saskatchewan Coal.
        Tricia Gibson. March 1983 (Price $7.50, 44 pages).

83-1   Development Options for Maritime Coal. John A. Dawson.
        January 1983 (Price $7.50, 42 pages).

Discussion Papers

83-1   The Alberta New Oil Royalty Formula: 74-04-01 to 82-12-31.
        Alan R. Webster. March 1983 (Price $6.00, 56 pages).

Presentations by Staff (available upon request)

87-4   Canadian Natural Gas Supply and its Inter-Relationship with
        the North American Natural Gas Market. Kevin Brown.
        Presentation to the Ninth Annual North American Meeting
        International Association of Energy Economists, Washington
        D.C., November 1987. Published in the Proceedings, November
        1987.

87-3   A Survey of Energy in Canada. Anthony E. Reinsch.
        Presentation to the World Energy Congress, Institute for
        Electrical and Electronic Engineering, Sao Paulo, Brazil,
        August 19-20, 1987.

87-2   World Oil Market Developments: Implications for the Canadian
        Crude Oil Supply-Demand Balance. Anthony E. Reinsch.
        Presentation to the AOSTRA conference, Advances in Petroleum
        Recovery and Upgrading Technology, Edmonton, Alberta, June
        2-3, 1987.

87-1   Industrial Cogeneration in Canada: Prospects and Perspec-
        tives. Anthony E. Reinsch. Presentation to the conference on
        Cogeneration and Parallel Electric Power Generation: The
        Opportunities, co-sponsored by the Canadian Energy Research
        Institute and the Ontario Ministry of Energy, Toronto,
        Ontario, March 30-31, 1987.

85-1   CANREM: An Integrated Model of Electric Utility Planning
        Processes. Gordon W. Douglas, Vaffi H. Poonja, and Ellen F.
        Battle. Presentation to the Canadian Operational Research
        Society, Halifax, May 23, 1985.

84-3   Canadian Electricity Exports: The New Opportunities. Ellen
        F. Battle and Gordon W. Douglas. Presentation to the
        International Association of Energy Economists, San Francisco,
        November 6, 1984.

84-2   Canadian Natural Gas Export Policies and Prospects. G. E.
        Angevine. Presentation to Platt's International Gas
        Conference, Rome, October 29, 1984.

84-1   The CANREM Model: Model Structure, User Experience and
        Potential Applications. Gordon W. Douglas, Gordon S.
        Gislason, and Ellen F. Battle. Presentation to the Canadian
        Electrical Association Meetings, Edmonton, March 15, 1984.

83-5   Canadian Energy Issues and Outlook. Douglas J. Haughey.
        Paper presented to the Institute of Internal Auditors,
        Calgary, October 18, 1983.

83-4   Energy Pricing in the World and Canada. James A. MacMillan.
        Paper presented to the Canadian Chapter of the International
        Association of Energy Economists, Toronto, May 20, 1983.

83-3   Economic and Financial Implications of Lower Oil Prices.
        Walter Haessel. Paper presented at a conference on The Impact
        of Lower Oil Prices, sponsored by Data Resources of Canada,
        Sheraton Centre, Toronto, April 14, 1983.

83-2   Net Regional and National Benefits of Canadian Electricity
        Exports. Gordon S. Gislason, Ellen F. Battle, and Gordon W.
        Douglas. Paper presented to the Canadian Electrical
        Association Generation System Planning and Operation
        Subsection, Vancouver, March 21, 1983.

83-1   Household Energy Costs: Recent Developments and Options for
        the Future. G. E. Angevine. Notes for Remarks at the "New
        Neighbourhood Forum," sponsored by the Ontario Ministry of
        Housing and Municipal Affairs, Toronto, January 31, 1983.

Proceedings

Cogeneration and Parallel Electric Power Generation: The
Opportunities. March 1987. Photocopies of available papers
($75.00/set; $20/individual paper, 469 pages) ISBN 0-92522-43-7.

International Oil and Gas Markets Conference. September 1986.
Photocopies of available papers ($100/set; $25/individual paper).

Oil and Gas Markets Conference. September 1985. Photocopies of
available papers ($100/set; $25/individual paper).

Petroleum and Natural Gas Markets Conference. September 1984.
Photocopies of available papers ($100/set; $25/individual paper).

International Gas Markets Conference. Proceedings of a Conference held
on September 26, 1983, Calgary, Alberta. Edited by Shane S. Streifel
(Price $45.00, 247 pages) ISBN 0-920522-33-5.

Annual Report

Board of Directors' Report for the Year Ended March 31, 1987.